A NOVEL BASED ON THE LIFE OF
FRANK CAPRA

THE
EMBRACE
— OF —
HOPE

Kate Fuglei

THE
MENTORIS
PROJECT

Mentoris Project
745 South Sierra Madre Drive
San Marino, CA 91108

Copyright © 2021 Mentoris Project

Cover photo: PictureLux / The Hollywood Archive / Alamy Stock Photo

Cover design: Suzanne Turpin

More information at www.mentorisproject.org

ISBN: 978-1-947431-39-3

Library of Congress Control Number: 2021918799

All net proceeds from the sale of this book will be donated to the Mentoris Project whose mission is to support educational initiatives that foster an appreciation of history and culture to encourage and inspire young people to create a stronger future.

The Mentoris Project is a series of novels and biographies about the lives of great men and women who have changed history through their contributions as scientists, inventors, explorers, thinkers, and creators. The Barbera Foundation sponsors this series in the hope that, like a mentor, each book will inspire the reader to discover how she or he can make a positive contribution to society.

Contents

Foreword

First and foremost, Mentor was a person. We tend to think of the word *mentor* as a noun (a mentor) or a verb (to mentor), but there is a very human dimension embedded in the term. Mentor appears in Homer's *Odyssey* as the old friend entrusted to care for Odysseus's household and his son Telemachus during the Trojan War. When years pass and Telemachus sets out to search for his missing father, the goddess Athena assumes the form of Mentor to accompany him. The human being welcomes a human form for counsel. From its very origins, becoming a mentor is a transcendent act; it carries with it something of the holy.

The Mentoris Project sets out on an Athena-like mission: We hope the books that form this series will be an inspiration to all those who are seekers, to those of the twenty-first century who are on their own odysseys, trying to find enduring principles that will guide them to a spiritual home. The stories that comprise the series are all deeply human. These books dramatize the lives of great men and women whose stories bridge the ancient and the modern, taking many forms, just as Athena did, but always holding up a light for those living today.

Whether in novel form or traditional biography, these books

plumb the individual characters of our heroes' journeys. The power of storytelling has always been to envelop the reader in a vivid and continuous dream, and to forge a link with the subject. Our goal is for that link to guide the reader home with a new inspiration.

What is a mentor? A guide, a moral compass, an inspiration. A friend who points you toward true north. We hope that the Mentoris Project will become that friend, and it will help us all transcend our daily lives with something that can only be called holy.

—Robert J. Barbera, Founder, The Mentoris Project
—Ken LaZebnik, Founding Editor, The Mentoris Project

Chapter One

THE EMBRACE OF COURAGE

Francesco Rosario Capra spent May 10, 1903, in sick bay. It was eight days before his sixth birthday. The rest of his family was also ill and had been since they boarded the ship to America. Everyone except their mother, Rosaria, called Sarrida, was prostrate in their tiny room in steerage. Frankie had a temperature and so was sent to sick bay.

He lay two decks above his family on a scratchy gray wool blanket with "SS *Germania*" printed in large letters across the bottom half. If he leaned on his elbow and raised his head, he could peer out the dirty round window. He lay on his side and watched the rolling waves. He could hear them slap against the side of the ship. A spider spun a web on the windowsill. It climbed slowly, patiently up the skein of the web, sometimes falling back but never giving up. Concentrating on the spider and its efforts took Frankie's mind off the constant pain in his stomach.

His mother came to visit from steerage every day. She advised the nurse to put a slice of raw potato on his forehead.

Frankie watched the nurse nod her head with her arms crossed. When his mother left, the nurse shook her head and dismissed the old-world advice.

The Capra family—Sarrida Capra and her husband, Salvatore, called Turridu, son Tony, daughter Anne, and little Frankie—had boarded the steamship *Germania* in Naples. An older son, Ben, was already in America. Ben lived in Los Angeles. Two older daughters remained in Bisacquino, a small village in Sicily. The Capra family had lived for generations in Bisacquino. Sarrida's children were baptized and socialized in the Catholic church there. Ben's letters from Los Angeles, the City of Angels, had urged them to come to America. He repeatedly called it the land of opportunity, the land of the immigrant, the land of hope.

Sarrida was the most interested in America. Ben's letters had filled her with ambition. She saw opportunity and a future for her children. Turridu resisted the move to America. He loved the social life of Bisacquino and the evening musicales spent harmonizing with his brothers, sitting and telling stories. He loved the rolling hills and the orchards that produced the fruit he loved to eat. He saw nothing wrong with staying in the village forever. But his wife prevailed. Ben sent money from America. The Capras cobbled together what they could, packed a cart with clothing and belongings, and bought five steerage tickets on the *Germania*.

On the docks in Naples, Turridu put his arm around five-year-old Frankie's shoulders and said, "On the other side of the horizon, Cici, is America, the land of your mother's dreams and streets paved with gold. Remember your name: Capra. It is the root of the word capricious and also of Capricorn. We are people who are determined but are also willing to change. There is nobility in that, Cici."

"Stop filling his head with nonsense," said his wife. "I don't believe in dreams. I believe in practicality. There is nothing noble about being poor and lazy. Our children would never make anything of themselves in Bisacquino. They'd end up sitting around strumming guitars and doing nothing, like you and your friends. We will never get there if we don't get rid of some of the weight in these bags. You have packed too much. We need to stop talking and get to work."

Everything Sarrida threw out, Turridu begged to keep. A loud argument ensued, and fellow passengers stared.

They left behind a framed painting of the little church in Bisacquino, four jars of olives neighbors had given them as a going-away gift, and three bottles of wine. As they climbed the ramp to go into the ship, the Capra family shaded their eyes to watch the first class passengers board. They were greeted warmly by the captain. A band played a lively tune to welcome them to the upper deck. Flags fluttered gaily on ropes that ringed the perimeter. The steerage passengers were herded onto the ship like so many cattle. Turridu ran back to snatch a bottle of wine that Sarrida had left dockside. He felt he would need it. The wine was quickly confiscated by a surly deck hand.

"You never listen to me," said Sarrida, shaking her head.

"I listen to you too much," answered her husband.

A deckhand flicked a thumb toward a steel door and slammed it open. He said not a word but ambled off down the dark hallway. It was clear this was to be the Capras' home for the thirteen-day voyage. They surveyed the tiny room with bunk beds bolted to the wall. A yellow bulb hanging on a wire provided the only light. There was no window. A wooden bucket that stood in the corner was, they supposed, their washstand. No one knew where the bathroom was. They would soon need it. The ship pulled out with a lurch from the dock. Before it reached the open sea, everyone but Sarrida had retched into the bucket.

The Capras were confined by illness to their quarters for much of the journey, with Turridu the most affected. They lay prone on their cots, which were covered with scratchy wool blankets. A constant blast of fetid air came from the boiler room. There was no air circulation. Food had to be brought down from the deck above. Frankie watched his mother climb up the narrow iron ladder to the next deck with an empty wooden tray. She returned a while later with the tray laden with bowls. She somehow balanced it with one hand while climbing down the ladder, holding her long skirt in the other. For the first ten days of the voyage, Frankie watched her perform this feat of love three times a day, never spilling a drop. He was full of admiration. Then his temperature sent him to sick bay.

On the thirteenth day at sea, Frankie was deemed well enough to return to his family in steerage. As he climbed down the ladder, he heard his father say they were nearing America. There was a jolt of energy in the squalid room as Sarrida ordered everyone to fold their clothing and stuff it neatly into bags. The clothes were, for the most part, filthy. The Capras had been unable to bathe since they left Bisacquino.

"It is nothing to be ashamed of," Sarrida said. "We will hold our heads high nonetheless. We are no different from any of the other people in steerage."

"Soon Lady Liberty will smile on us," Turridu promised.

"What if she spits on us?" said Tony, who received a quick box on his ear from his mother. It was quickly followed by a bear hug. Tony was Sarrida's favorite.

The ocean was beginning to calm and there was a general feeling of bustle in the dark hallway. A loud horn began to blow and Frankie could feel the ship slowing. He still felt weak and tired and lay back on his bunk.

"Get up, lazy!" said Tony, leaning over him with his face inches away. "It's time to see Lady Liberty! I'm told she has a good figure," he said, cupping his hands suggestively on his chest. Frankie looked away.

"Aw, you are a wimp," Tony conceded and raced up the ladder to the deck, following the rest of his family. Turridu stayed behind and lifted Frankie to his shoulders so he could just peek out at the sky.

"See, Cici?" he said. "There she is, Lady Liberty. Isn't she beautiful?"

Frankie saw her. She was framed for just a moment by the

opening at the top of the ladder. Right in the center. She held a torch. The morning sun glinted off her steady gaze. She slowly passed out of sight as the ship made its way into the harbor.

"You are now in the country of freedom and opportunity, Cici," said his father. "Here you can be anything you want to be. You are going to be a great American. Now go and wipe the vomit off your chin. Stand up straight. Never forget your roots—the people of Sicily, of Bisacquino. We're here."

A cacophony greeted the Capras as they lurched down the ramp, clutching their belongings. It overwhelmed them. Frankie gazed across the water at the buildings of lower Manhattan. Their tops seemed to touch the clouds. Frankie had never seen anything like them.

Frankie's heart was pounding with anticipation. But exhaustion soon overcame him as he stood with his family in a huge crowd of people. He heard sounds and languages that were strange and guttural. Women carried bags filled with feather ticking and dented pots. They clutched their children. The children grew restless. Some threw tantrums. Many were hungry, and although Frankie could not understand their languages, he knew their pleading was for food. Frankie watched the scenes of human interaction with interest. He realized that though their languages were different, they were all, in essence, the same, with the same needs, the same wants.

Hours went by as they stood in line. They finally moved up to a row of benches and sat there for several more hours. Then the Capra name was called.

A plump man wearing a blue suit and sporting a mustache that looked like a paintbrush called their name again. "Capra family! Get out your health tickets." Sarrida had them ready, tucked into the pocket of her apron. Another man walked up to them and gave each of them the once-over. He pinched Anne's cheek, and Turridu, offended at a stranger touching his daughter in such a familiar manner, began to protest. Frankie saw his mother slap his father's back. "Enough," she said, and shook her head vehemently. Frankie saw his father step back, head down. Apparently in America he had to accept such behavior. At least for now. They were all given cards and told to go to another area of the registry hall.

After more hours of waiting, the Capra family was allowed outside. Ben had told them in a letter to hire a cart to take them directly to Grand Central Terminal. "You'll be tired," he wrote, "but you can sleep on the train. Less expensive than finding a hotel for five people in Manhattan." The cart, with an imperturbable driver, rattled through lower Manhattan. The streets teemed with people. Pushcarts lined the sidewalks. At times, it was impossible to move forward. The Atlantic Ocean had been replaced by a sea of people walking quickly and talking loudly. Carts full of colorful fruit tempted Tony. He jumped off at one point, grabbed three apples, and jumped back on, putting his finger to his lips.

The train proved to be worse, in some ways, than the ship. Frankie had imagined soft beds and steaming bowls of soup. The Capra family was directed to a train car with brown wooden benches. The ticket taker indicated there was no time to get food, as the departure was imminent. Tony decided he was so hungry he didn't care if the train left without him. He was determined to get food. Sarrida, who trusted her son's ingenuity more than her husband did, gave him one American dollar. Tony returned ten minutes later with four loaves of bread, salami, and a round of cheese. These he showered triumphantly on his grateful mother, along with a wink and the dollar she had given him. Sarrida patted her son's cheek and looked at her husband, saying, "Now this one knows how to survive."

Frankie, who was too young to leave his family and forage for food, stared out the train window at the scene on the track. He took in the young woman in a white silk dress kissing her child good-bye. He saw a beggar who kneeled on a board shaking a cup, then stood up and gingerly walked to a new spot when he thought no one was looking. Frankie looked in vain for the streets paved with gold as the train lurched across seemingly endless miles. He saw the smokestacks of Pennsylvania and tried to sound out the strange names of the rivers they crossed: Susquehanna. Monongahela.

They stopped in Chicago, and Turridu got off the train to buy day-old sandwiches, as a fellow passenger had told him they were cheaper and almost as good. Frankie could see his father through the dusty window of the train, bargaining with the sandwich man. The train began to lurch forward and the whistle blew. The bellman screamed out "All aboard!" The sandwich man snatched a dollar from Turridu, who ran toward the train to jump on before it picked up speed. He barely made it into the car with sandwiches spilling from his hands. As the hungry Capra children pounced on the stale sandwiches, Sarrida berated her husband for allowing himself to be cheated. They argued like this for miles as Frankie looked out the window at the ocean of waving wheat.

After a three-day train journey, the Capras arrived in the City of Angels. They were tired to the bone, dirty, and starved for something besides stale sandwiches. It was midday, and the sun beat down on them as they searched for Ben. Appearing from behind a fruit wagon, he was a welcome sight. He was bearing a basket of delicious edibles, which his family had not eaten in weeks. Frankie spied him first and ran ahead, eager to tell his big brother about the journey. Sarrida knelt on the platform at Union Station and bent down as if to kiss it. First, she crossed herself and thanked God for the safe arrival of her family in California after nearly twenty days of travel. Ben grabbed her by the shoulders just before her lips touched the filthy cement. "People don't do that here, Mamma," he said. "You are making a spectacle."

Frankie stared at a huge purple tree that stood against the blue sky. It had dropped its blossoms on the ground like a lavender carpet of welcome. The air was dry and it made Frankie's nose tickle. Ben gave him a bear hug, ruffled his dark curly hair, and said, "You have grown a little since I last saw you, but you will always be a squirt." Ben explained that the beautiful purple tree was a jacaranda. "Those blossoms you love are a mess to clean up. They stick to your shoes and they are not beautiful to me."

"Beautiful things can often create messes," agreed Turridu. "Just look at your mother and me."

Sarrida harrumphed and gave her husband a poke in the ribs.

"I'm teasing you, *mi amore*," said her husband. "Smell those orange blossoms in the air. If that isn't romantic, I don't know what is."

"I'm not looking for romance. I'm looking for food and a hot bath," replied his wife.

They made their way from Union Station down Alameda Street and up the hill to Castelar Street. Ben helped them climb the stairs to a small apartment. The windows faced the apartment next door. The air was stifling. As Sarrida surveyed the place, she said, "How am I going to feed and house five people living like this?"

"It was the best I could do with what I had, Mamma," said Ben. "It isn't far from downtown and the excitement of the city."

"Jobs are what we need," said Sarrida. "All of us. We can't make it unless we all contribute. America is not the land of slackers. All slackers can leave the premises," she said, eyeing her husband.

Sarrida immediately began to unpack, directing Anne to find a bucket for starting the laundry. She ordered her husband to find a grocery store with rice and beans. No meat. Just rice and beans.

Ben left his family to settle in, promising to return later. Frankie and Tony went exploring. They saw hordes of people of all races and descriptions. They saw Chinese, Africans, Mexicans, and Italians like themselves thronging a street called

Broadway that crossed Alameda. They ventured toward what Ben had called "downtown" and marveled at the cacophony, the teeming life of the city, and the energy that pulsed through the streets. Frankie and Tony watched the sun fade from gold to pink to purple over the turreted tower of the Los Angeles Times building. They saw crowds of boys their own age who seemed to be selling newspapers on the street corners nearby.

The night air was cool after the heat of the midday sun, and the two brothers returned home full of excitement to share what they had seen. They clambered up the narrow stairs in the dingy hallway and burst through the door. Sarrida boxed their ears for staying away so long. Dinner was rice and beans flavored with bacon fat that Sarrida had begged from the butcher down the street. They couldn't afford the bacon itself.

Sarrida Capra looked at her two young sons, her daughter Anne, and her husband. "If we are to survive here, we will all have to start working," she announced. "And that includes you two," she said, pointing at Tony and Frankie. "We are calling you Frank from now on," she told her youngest, "and you and your brother can find a way to contribute. No more wandering around scaring your mother half to death. There are no streets paved with gold, in case you haven't noticed."

Her face glistened with sweat. The air in the apartment was still. They could hear the clang of the streetcar running up Broadway. There was a loud altercation in the street below in a language none of them understood.

"America is not for the weak," Sarrida continued. "It is not going to give us anything. We have to work for it. Every hour.

Every day. Nothing comes for free. But the hope of something better will keep us going. It brought us from Sicily, and with the help of God it has gotten us here, and it will give us strength. Without hope, there is nothing. Now eat. But not too much. We have to save some for the morning."

After dinner, Sarrida insisted they walk to the Mission Plaza Church on Main Street and Sunset. They entered through a small courtyard. There was a large tree in the middle of the grassy interior that looked to Frank like an upended mop.

"It is called a palm tree," said Frank proudly. "Palm trees are beautiful, although not native to California."

"How do you know?" asked Tony derisively.

"I learned it myself today," said Frank, "I asked a man standing in front of the Los Angeles Times building. It's more than you could learn in a month." This provoked a scuffle that Turridu ended by kicking both of their backsides.

"You're in church," scolded Sarrida. "Behave respectfully, for God's sake." She lit a candle and they knelt. "May God protect us in America," she prayed. "Especially our children. May they grow to be proud, respected Americans."

"May they never forget who they are and where they came from," added Turridu.

In the weeks that followed in the early summer of 1903, the Capra family began to adjust to their new life. They came to see Los Angeles as a city in the midst of constant expansion. It had a center for commerce, a port in San Pedro, and a burgeoning attraction for tourists who came to the city for its sun and to Pasadena for its air, which was thought to be healthful and restorative. The business community was eager to promote California as a tourist mecca. Harris Gray Otis, or General Otis, as he was called due to his military exploits, was an owner of the *Los Angeles Times*. General Otis was a powerful promoter of his own business interests. A vehement anti-unionist, Otis used his newspaper to sell California to the world.

Even then, the city of Los Angeles had a curious relationship to immigrants. Their labor was needed to build the city. And yet, the image of a blonde, fair-skinned, orange-consuming, fresh-faced Californian was the one actively shown to the world. The wealthy Caucasian Protestants tended to congregate in Pasadena, while recent immigrants populated neighborhoods like Boyle Heights, to the east and just north of downtown, where the Capras first lived. The Capras settled in a neighborhood with a polyglot of races and nationalities who all shared common goals: to get out, to educate their children, and to better themselves.

Sarrida Capra's first job was picking strawberries. Then, on the advice of a neighbor, she found a job she would have for many years. She pasted labels on bottles of olive oil at the C. P. Grogan factory. There, she found camaraderie with other female immigrants. The factory was conveniently located blocks from her home on Castelar Street. She awoke early, put out bread to rise, made a stew to be reheated in the late afternoon, and left for her job by 7:00 a.m. This was the lot of a working immigrant woman with a family to support. Sarrida quickly stopped wearing the black dresses commonly worn by women her age in Italy. She adapted to American customs and dress, aided by her friends and colleagues at C. P. Grogan.

It was more difficult for Salvatore Capra to adjust. The grand life that had been promised by his son Ben failed to materialize. At one point, he was performing the only job it seemed he could do: shining shoes.

The Capra children were not exempt from the search for employment. Sarrida encouraged them daily to get out and make money. One neighbor told Tony and Frank that newsboys who hustled could do just that. Potential newsboys had to be at the Times building at 5:00 a.m. They picked up however many newspapers they thought they could sell. A boy could make a penny for each sale. Any leftover papers were charged against him. Success hinged, apparently, on the corner he worked. Fisticuffs often occurred over "ownership" of a good corner. The best corner downtown, by far, was in front of the Jonathan Club, the private club for the wealthiest and most powerful men in Los Angeles.

A month after arriving, Tony and Frank began to frequent the 5:00 a.m. dispersal in front of the Los Angeles Times building, and to move as fast as they could to claim the best spots. If they had papers left over at the end of the day, they would stage a mock fight to attract attention. When a crowd gathered, Frank would say in a pitiful voice, "He's beating me because I didn't sell all my papers!" His tearful visage always gulled the crowd into buying the leftovers. As the older brother, Tony took it upon himself to protect Frank from the other newsboys. They were a rough crowd of mixed ages and thought nothing of threatening or actually beating another newsboy they suspected of trying to muscle in on their profits.

One day, Tony watched Frank sell a paper to an amused member of the Jonathan Club. "Smart kid," said the member, ruffling Frank's hair and giving him a large tip. Tony felt humiliated and took it out on Frank. "If you are so damned smart," he said, "you can go out tomorrow by yourself."

"I will," said Frank. "And I'll sell a whole lot more than you." This prompted a chase around the rickety kitchen table, with Tony kicking Frank and Sarrida screaming that they stop.

The next morning, while it was still dark outside, Frank left the apartment on Castelar Street. It was already warm. Santa Ana winds were blowing, bringing dust from the desert and, some said, crazy behavior. Frank had never been out this early without his brother. He hurried right and down dark, deserted Alameda Street toward the Los Angeles Time building at First and Spring Streets. He had fifty cents in his pocket, a fortune to a six-year-old. He planned on using it to buy a stack of newspapers to sell in front of the Jonathan Club as the businessmen made their way to breakfast meetings inside. Frank's heart pounded as he rushed down the dark street. Suddenly, he heard the familiar voices of two of the older newsboys, one of whom had already been in a fight with Tony.

"Hey, runt! Where you going so early? Where's your ugly brother?"

Frank heard the crash of glass and realized they had thrown a bottle at him. He began to run. There were three of them, all twice as tall as Frank, and the click of their shoes on the pavement made a staccato sound.

The tallest, a boy with a pockmarked face, threw his arm

around Frank's neck and dragged him roughly into an alley. He grabbed Frank by the front of his trousers, which were hand-me-downs from Tony and much too big. Then he punched Frank in the stomach with such force Frank let out a gasp of air. He punched Frank a second time. Frank felt the impact as though it had gone all the way to his spine. He collapsed onto the concrete, and his attacker kicked him in the knees while leaning down close to Frank's ear. His breath smelled like sour onions.

"This is what we do to little dagos that try to horn in on our territory," the boy hissed.

It was over in a moment. Frank's attacker rejoined his friends, saying, "The little squirt got what was coming to him." They smashed another bottle against the brick wall of a grocery store that was just opening. The owner came out screaming and brandishing a broom. He saw Frank staggering around the corner and thought at first he was part of the gang. When he noticed the gash on Frank's cheek and realized he was looking at a very young boy, he reached for Frank's hand. Frank shook his head and turned toward home.

His stomach ached where he had been punched. He stopped to vomit the hard roll and milk he had eaten before leaving. Then a thought came to him. He didn't know where it came from, but it was clear and strong, like a voice in his head: *I will never run from anyone again. You can't run from what is ugly. You have to face it.*

With that, Frank turned, retraced his steps, and soon found himself at the Los Angeles Times building. The boys who attacked him were nowhere to be seen. The warm Santa Ana winds rushed through the streets and made the palm trees sway. The last star in the Los Angeles sky was fading. Frank felt dried blood on his face and wiped it with a dirty handkerchief. He jingled the fifty cents in his pocket and stepped up to the wagon that held stacks of newspapers. He was ready to make some sales. His childhood ended that day, but in its place arose a stubborn adult resilience.

Frank made his way to the corner of Sixth and Main, near Angels Flight. It wasn't the Jonathan Club, but he would still make plenty of sales. He walked by drunks lying in the gutter and disheveled women leaning against the streetlights that were just beginning to turn off. He didn't know why the women were there; he was still too young. But the despair and weariness in their faces touched him.

As he neared the corner, a legless beggar who got around on a platform with wheels greeted Frank by name. "Frankie, it's gonna be a good day! The Santa Anas always bring a change. You'll see, kid." Frank found a way to smile. No matter how bad his life was, there was always someone who had it worse.

Frank and Tony continued to compete for the best spots. Frank understood that he needed Tony for protection. He decided not to antagonize his older, brawny brother. Tony continued to resent his younger brother's obvious intelligence, which was noticed by teachers at Castelar Elementary. They singled out Frank early on, choosing him to recite the Pledge of Allegiance on opening day of first grade. The whole family turned out to witness this expression of pride in becoming an American. Although proud of their son, his parents also realized this was the first of many steps that would take him away from them and their identity as Sicilian immigrants. Also, Sarrida was more interested in saving money and buying a house. The education of her children came second.

Her dream was realized in 1905, when the Capra family purchased a three-bedroom home on Albion Street in Lincoln Heights, a neighborhood that bordered downtown Los Angeles to the east. Sarrida was pleased, finally, with this first true step toward achieving the American dream. Turridu, who still longed for the orchards of Italy, planted fruit trees in the small backyard and on the parkway. The front porch became a spot for weekend gatherings and musicales. The step up in living situation did nothing to lessen the arguments between the couple, many of which centered around money. There never seemed to be enough.

Frank attended Griffin Elementary in Lincoln Heights from 1905 to 1911. One of his teachers, Jean McDaniel, took a special interest in him, giving him books from her home library. Frank often read late into the night. One night, he became lost in the adventures of the *Three Musketeers*, read until almost dawn, and slept through the wake-up time for his paper route.

"Get up, you lazy idiot!" Tony yelled, smacking Frank on the head and kicking the book under the bed they shared.

"Wasting time like that will ruin your eyes and you'll end up with nothing," agreed Sarrida. "Get up and get out! You think money grows on trees? There are newsboys standing in line who want to help their families. Don't you?"

She shoved a piece of bread slathered with sardines at Frank.

Tony snatched it away as they ran down the stairs of the porch onto Albion Street. The sun was just making its way to the tops of the palm trees.

"Little runts like you don't need to eat," Tony said, downing the bread and sardines with one bite. Frank chased him, jumping on his brother's back. They tumbled to the ground. Sarrida ran out of the house, clapping them both on the back.

"What did I ever do to deserve sons like you? God, tell me, what?" she screamed dramatically.

"Oh, Ma, we're going," said Tony, dusting off his pants. "Come on, runt."

When Frank was a year away from graduation from Griffin Elementary, Jean McDaniel invited him to her home for dinner. The occasion was the source of endless jokes and taunts from Tony, who was no longer going to school, having punched a teacher. Frank ignored his brother and dug out a clean shirt from a pile on the floor of their shared bedroom.

The McDaniel home in Boyle Heights was painted white and had a white picket fence surrounding the front yard. Mr. McDaniel answered the door with a smile and showed Frank into the dining room, where a porcelain soup tureen sat on a lace tablecloth. Jean McDaniel brought out a platter bearing a roast chicken surrounded by vegetables. Her husband served the soup, and they ate it with special soup spoons.

Beside Frank's plate was a cloth napkin edged in lace. Frank didn't know what to do with it at first and stuck it in the front of his collar, as he had seen men do in downtown coffee shops. The McDaniels had two older daughters who asked Frank polite questions. There were no arguments. No teasing. No insults, loud voices, or threats. As the light outside faded, Jean McDaniel lit two white candles in brass holders. The glow gave even more warmth to her kindly countenance. The table was cleared and tea was served in china cups.

"Frank, I want to encourage you to go to high school," she said. "You are excellent at math and science, and I know you have an interest in history. Manual Arts is a new high school not far from downtown. They have a new administration, a very forward-thinking one, and . . . ." Here Jean McDaniel paused and stirred sugar into her teacup. Then she continued.

"Members of the PTA and I know you work a newspaper job every day of the week. We've gathered together some contributions from the committee, and we want to give them to you so you don't have to work so hard. For this last year of elementary school, we want to give you the gift of being able to be a student, a boy, without having the burden of constant work."

Realizing the kindness and generosity of the gesture brought a lump to Frank's throat. At the same time, he felt a rush of shame. His heart started pounding and he began to sweat. He could feel his cheeks flushing. He looked down at the thick flowered carpet at his feet as if memorizing the swirls and patterns in the wool tufts. Jean McDaniel patted his head and said, "Well, you think about it, Frank. Just think about it."

As Frank walked down the brick path in front of the McDaniel home and clicked the gate shut, he gazed for a moment at the serene scene through the front window. Mr. McDaniel sat puffing on a meerschaum pipe and reading the newspaper.

Jean McDaniel sipped tea and graded papers. This was America. He decided he was going to change his name from Francesco Rosario Capra to Frank Russell Capra. No matter what argument or insult his own family offered about high school, he was determined to go.

Frank Russell Capra was in America, and he was going to pursue his own freedom and happiness. It was his right now. And no one was going to stop him.

On February 6, 1911, Frank Capra sat at the back of the auditorium assembly at Manual Arts High School. It was his first day of school as a member of the Winter 1915 class. He had graduated from Griffin Elementary the week before. Frank wanted to observe his fellow students en masse, hoping this might quell the feeling of intimidation that sat like a rock in his stomach.

He arrived at Manual Arts, which was situated south and east of downtown Los Angeles, by leaving the house at 5:00 a.m. and taking two trolleys. Newly built as a second high school close to downtown, Manual Arts was at the edge of a large bean field near the University of Southern California. Frank had to cross the field alone in the pitch dark.

His family agreed to let him go to high school only if he continued to contribute to the family coffers. Jean McDaniel helped him find a job as a janitor at the school. On his first day, Frank arrived early for his daily shift, emptying trash cans and cleaning blackboards at the direction of the surly head of maintenance. He carried a clean shirt to change into after he sweated through his work shirt. After his shift, he wandered the halls, taking in the arched doorways and the large plaza with a fountain. He ended his tour at the auditorium that would soon be filled with his peers.

At 8:00 a.m., the students began filing in. They came in groups of four and five, many arm in arm, waving greetings to one another. Some searched desperately for someone they knew. Frank had never seen so many beautiful girls. They wore pink, yellow, and white linen dresses and looked for all the world like moving flower gardens. Rocky Washington, a friend from Lincoln Heights, slid in beside Frank, who had never been more grateful for a familiar face.

"Those are the Pasadena girls," Rocky said. "You can tell them by their blonde hair and perfection. But you can't tell one from the other. They are sort of all the same."

Frank laughed in agreement and wondered what his mother and his sister Anne would think about these female clouds of perfection, so different in every way from the neighborhood girls he was used to.

A tall, distinguished-looking man wearing a bow tie and sporting a crown of gray hair walked to the podium.

"That's our principal, Dr. Albert Wilson," said Rocky. "He runs a tight ship. Don't try to pull anything on him."

"Dear scholars," Dr. Wilson began. "For scholars are what you are. You have been chosen by fate to come together here, at this temple of learning, from all parts of this great, great city, the City of Angels. Our city is on its way to becoming the best example of what makes this country great. From Lincoln Heights, Angelino Heights, Boyle Heights, Pasadena, Alhambra and beyond, you have all gathered here to learn, to grow, to bestow on us your joy in living. It is our job to bring peace to this world and lead our great American communities.

"Manual Arts can only be the sum total of what you bring to us: your passions and interests," Dr. Wilson continued. "You are all destined to be what we produce here at Manual Arts. You are the Model Ts of this great city and we, your teachers, are only here to polish your hubcaps. Some people call me 'out of the box.' That is absolutely true. I have brought together here, at Manual Arts, the finest teachers who are here to bring out the best in you, to help you create your own American destiny."

Frank had no idea what to make of the speech. He had never heard anything remotely like it. He had never been addressed by an adult or any person of authority with such warmth and respect. He felt he was going to like Manual Arts.

The years at Manual Arts, with its progressive administration and combination of students from all income levels, gave Frank further education in the lives of the haves and the have-nots. Along with Rocky Washington, there were other students from his neighborhood, such as Jimmy Doolittle, whose family had come over from Ireland. Doolittle would grow up to be one of the most honored pilots in history. For now, he was a jocular teenager and a fellow member, with Frank, of the Manual Arts gymnastics team.

Then there were the blue bloods of Pasadena, who moved through the universe of Manual Arts with a physical ease and confidence born of security and entitlement. Frank watched them each morning from his perch in the window of the janitor's room. They alighted from fancy cars on the sidewalk in front of the school, kissing their loving parents good-bye. "They are at ease in the world. It is their oyster. All is right in their world," thought Frank as he changed from his dirty work shirt into a clean one he had ironed that morning.

All was not right in Frank's world. He still had to do the janitor job every day before school. He also continued to work selling newspapers with his brother Tony. And, taking after his father, he had picked up enough musical skill to play a banjo. He found work on the weekend playing at bars on Central Avenue. There were upstairs rooms at some of the bars, and Frank was now old enough to understand what happened there. The schedule he kept, and the panoply of lives and people he encountered, made him wise beyond his years. His family still harangued him constantly about contributing money.

Despite all this, Frank found the time and energy to be involved in activities at Manual Arts. He desperately wanted to be part of the life at the school, to reach beyond the confines of his family. He learned to manage his time and to switch between jobs and people with grace and dexterity. He joined the Delphic Society and pursued his interest in science. He had neither the time nor the money for the dating rituals that were intrinsic to teenage life. He felt he stood outside the window, always looking in. His life, full of encounters with jaded newspapermen, fellow janitors, and ladies of the night from the Central Avenue bars, was a far cry from the lives of the popular, well-scrubbed Pasadena blue bloods. For the most part, they shunned him and Frank gave them a wide berth. He kept his life in Lincoln Heights and his array of jobs secret and separate from his life at Manual Arts.

One of his favorite teachers was Rob Wagner, a visual artist, illustrator, and designer who taught English. Wagner had moved from the East Coast to California for his wife's health. She had passed away, leaving him with two young children to raise. Dr. Wilson had seen in Wagner the passion and energy that he felt would inspire students at the newly forming high school. Wagner was a true Bohemian and lived in a house full of art. He encouraged his students to think unconventionally and to write about their own lives and experiences.

Frank never forgot the day he met Rob Wagner. Striding into the room wearing a billowing white shirt, Wagner swept onto the small stage at the front, already speaking.

"You must know who you are and what you want to say," he told them. When he spoke, he gesticulated wildly and ran his hands through his hair, which stood on end. "Let us throw out convention. Rule-followers and kiss-asses, there is the door! I'm looking into each of your faces and I see thousands of stories behind those eyes. Do not write what you think I want to hear. Write what you know, what you feel, what you dream.

"You there, the gentleman knitting his brows and looking at me as if I am out of my mind," Wagner said, pointing to Frank. "Yes, you. The one who clearly thinks I am off my rocker. What makes you tick?"

Frank was dumbfounded. Did Wagner really want an answer?

"I want to tell stories!" Frank blurted out. "That's why I'm here. That's what makes me tick. Stories about what I've seen and heard and . . . and felt." Frank had no idea where the words came from. Now they hung in the air of the classroom. Forty other students and Rob Wagner had heard.

"What's your name, young man?" asked Wagner.

"Frank. Frank Capra."

"Well, Frank Capra," said Wagner, "I have a feeling we are going to get along just fine. I want to hear all your stories. The world does, too. That is what makes us human; the coming together to share all we have seen, felt, heard. Don't remain silent, Frank. This is not a class for remaining silent. Ever. Find a partner. Start telling them one of your stories. The only rule: for God's sake, don't bore them."

The girl seated in front of Frank turned around. She had round cornflower-blue eyes and pale blonde hair that framed her face. She was enchanting. She had never before spoken to Frank. "Hi there, Frank Capra," she said with a grin, "I'm Mary, and you are going to tell me your story."

Frank swallowed hard. She was so beautiful it was hard to think of one word, let alone string any together. He began tentatively, but soon became caught up in telling his story so Mary would feel she was right there inside it. He told her the story of an exhausted immigrant family on a train, starving hungry, the father being cheated out of his last dollar by a sandwich seller, and the matriarch of the family excoriating her husband. Mary hung on every word. Her eyes filled with tears when he described the final image.

"Why did the wife yell at and humiliate her husband?" Mary asked. "It wasn't really his fault."

Frank shrugged, "Because she was tough. And she was protecting her children, I guess, telling her husband he needed to have a backbone."

"Is it a true story, Frank Capra?" asked Mary in a low tone. She had moved closer and he could see the dark lashes that framed her blue eyes. He lost himself in them.

"Class is concluded for today," announced Rob Wagner, "but as an artist, you must never stop observing, taking notes, living, for God's sake, LIVING. Live in the here and now. Yesterday is the past. Tomorrow is only a dream. You are young. Live! No; better yet, go out and create. And bring what you create here to share."

Frank spent his years at Manual Arts moving between the stressful life of the Capra family, perpetually struggling, and the wider world of education and opportunity. He spent less and less time at home, managing to escape some of the tension. The schism between life at home and the life he led away from home grew larger. Frank felt like an outsider in his own family as well as at his school. The only time the aching feeling went away was when he lost himself in his work. Sometimes, reading a book, completing an experiment in the lab, or working in Rob Wagner's class, he forgot he was little Frankie Capra, the outsider.

As graduation approached in 1915, his teachers, like those at Griffin Elementary, began to encourage him to continue his education. His family's derision for college was even more strident than it had been for high school. Sarrida was anxious to have her son making a living working full-time. She saw no practical purpose in a college education.

Frank's daily walks across the bean field to Manual Arts had long been a welcome break between home and the world of his high school. Roads were being blacktopped, and the city of Los Angeles was growing up around what had once been fields and empty lots. To the south, he could see the spires of the University of Southern California, a private university that to Frank seemed unattainable. But Rob Wagner had told him about a college in Pasadena that had the lofty aim of rivaling the University of Chicago in the humanities and competing with MIT in science. Its name was Throop College of Technology. (Today it's known as the California Institute of Technology, or Caltech.) Wagner encouraged Frank to apply.

Wagner also urged his students to see a full-length film directed by D. W. Griffith that was opening at the Clune's Theatre. The auditorium seated 2,700, and on the night Frank attended in March 1915, every seat was taken. The impresario Billy Clune hired a full orchestra to accompany the film, called *Birth of a Nation*. Frank had seen films before, but this was the first time he had done so with a full audience in a movie palace. He was disturbed by the images of violence and racism. He was equally mesmerized by the film and the way the audience reacted. The unique power of capturing the attention of so many people for two hours in the dark impressed him deeply. The film struck Frank as overblown and at times inauthentic. But the audience's response was remarkable.

Frank's graduation from Manual Arts provided the opportunity for a celebration at the Capra home in Lincoln Heights. Although they were not always supportive of his decision to attend high school, the Capra family looked on their son with pride. There were tables of pastries, bowls of pasta, and, of course, music provided by Turridu and his friends from the neighborhood.

"We came here twelve years ago with only what we could bring in a cart," Turridu said, wiping tears from his eyes. "Now we have a high school graduate. And more great things are happening for the Capra family. I am taking over as manager at Churchill Ranch in Sierra Madre, and I will be able to work full-time with fruits and vegetables, and be outside in nature with trees and the sun and the sky . . . where I was meant to be. And my son Francesco, for he will always be Francesco to me, will be attending Throop College of Technology in Pasadena in the fall."

There was the sound of a pitcher being dropped. This was the first Sarrida Capra had heard of either her husband's new job or Frank's college plans. A loud argument began that lasted late into the night.

Just after graduation, in May of 1915, Rob Wagner was commissioned to produce and direct a film called *Our Wonderful Schools*. He used Manual Arts as a location, and Frank visited the set one evening in late spring. His classmate Mary was also there. The two of them were amused as they watched Rob run from the director's chair to the set, brandishing a bullhorn as he herded students who were being used as extras.

Frank and Mary stood back from the mayhem. A spring

breeze rustled the palm trees above them. The bright lights from the set illuminated the night sky.

"My friend, you would be good at this," said Mary.

"At what?" said Frank, looking at her. He wasn't thinking about anything but the light shining into her blue eyes.

"At this. Directing. You are so organized and intelligent, and anyone who can work three jobs as well as do what you do . . . I believe you can do anything." She lifted up her face and it was illuminated, briefly, by a klieg light.

Frank had never wanted anything more than to kiss her at that moment. But she had called him "friend." He was too afraid. The moment passed.

Chapter Two

THE EMBRACE OF BELONGING

Salvatore Capra stood on the front porch of the house at Churchill Ranch. He surveyed the valley laid out before him. A white clapboard house stood behind him. To Turridu, it represented the American dream. He did not own it. He was merely renting it as part of his new job as manager of Churchill Ranch. But some days, he imagined that the land and the house were his.

He took a deep breath and looked out at the rows of mature lemon trees to his left. The young lemon trees he had spent the day planting were in neat rows to his right. Beyond was the town of Sierra Madre, with the San Gabriel Mountains in the distance. He could see Mount Baldy surrounded by soft white clouds. It reminded him of Bisacquino and the Apennines and the country he had left behind twelve years ago. The early evening breeze ruffled the leaves of the trees. He looked at his hands and smiled. The dirt of the day, a day of complete pleasure, was ground into the crevasses of his sixty-three-year-old hands.

After nearly a decade of living in America, in Los Angeles, in a house surrounded by cement, Turridu had found a measure of freedom by renting and agreeing to manage Churchill Ranch near Sierra Madre, a small town east of Pasadena. His son Ben and daughter-in-law Mary, with their son, Sam, came to live with him. Sarrida visited on weekends but refused to move to what she called "nowhere." "I didn't move to America to live in an orchard," she said. Her husband didn't like the arrangement. His own father and grandfather would never have allowed it in the old country. They would have insisted their wives go with them. But this was the new country. Women behaved differently here. Turridu decided to accept it.

He had found a deep happiness already, a peace and serenity in the soil, the sky, and in spending his days growing things. From the porch, Turridu awaited the arrival of Frank, his favorite son. Frank was the one in which he took the most pride. He was proud of all of his sons: Ben, who had made his way to America first, and Tony, the resourceful, practical one. Tony was just like his mother. But Frank was something else. He was living with his father while attending Throop. Whoever thought a son of his would go to college? This was the best part of America. There were already piles of books in the house. Books that Salvatore couldn't read. But Frank could, and his father secretly marveled at the intensity of his son's focus as he studied every night.

Frank was in his first year at Throop. Turridu scanned the horizon, listening for the putt-putt of Frank's scooter on the hill leading to the ranch house. Soon, against the fading light of the September evening, a cloud of dust formed as the scooter made its way up the hill. It was less than ten miles from Throop in Pasadena to Sierra Madre, but it took Frank nearly an hour to make the trip, dodging trucks and automobiles. It didn't matter. Frank was usually elated when he arrived, eager to share his day.

Frank had spent the entire summer of 1915 toiling like a dog, stuffing newspapers at the *Los Angeles Times*, working as a night watchman and fix-it man at Western Pipe and Steel, a job he still held, and playing gigs at bars on Central Avenue. He had managed to put together tuition and give some extra money to his mother, who always needed it. Even Tony had been impressed.

It hadn't occurred to Frank, until he walked through the brick archway leading to the main auditorium at Throop, that all he had worked and hoped for with regard to college might not materialize. He had worked so hard to get to Throop that he hadn't spent much time thinking about how it would actually feel once he got there.

The opening speech by Dr. James A. B. Scherer, the president of the college, dispelled his fears. The feeling at Throop was entirely different from that of Manual Arts. The emphasis was on intellectual pursuits and the life of the mind. In his speech, Scherer spoke about the importance of humanism, the whole person, life and the arts in the education of a scientist. He reminded them of a speech Theodore Roosevelt had given at Throop in 1911. Roosevelt had urged his listeners to aspire to become both scientists and humanists, the "hundredth men" who would use their intelligence and moral purpose to build a better world. Frank immediately felt inspired and less intimidated than he had been at Manual Arts.

During his first days at Throop, Frank was introduced to poetry and great literature by Clinton Kelly Judy, a Harvard-educated professor who strode into the classroom reading aloud from Ralph Waldo Emerson. Judy made poetry come alive. Frank's room at the ranch was soon filled with books, which he began collecting, and poems, which he began to write. As the semester went on, Frank spent less time at Churchill Ranch. He saw less of his mother and sister Anne as he became ensconced in both the intellectual and social life at Throop. He joined the Gnome Fraternity and attended parties and dances when he could. His work at Western Pipe and Steel and his waiter job at the Throop cafeteria left little time for socializing, but now that he was accepted and respected by his fellow students, he had a greater desire to socialize.

Frank had reached his adult height of a compact five feet, four inches. He had also grown into his face, which was handsome, with a high forehead, square jaw, and dark eyes that glittered with curiosity. Young women at dances found him to be a lively companion and a dancing partner full of rhythm and grace. For Frank, seeing the comparative ease of the lives of the wealthier students still chafed. But it seemed to matter less as they began to recognize him for his intelligence. He could also be fun. He played the ukulele and sang. His energy was infectious. His peers understood that he had to work to pay for his education, and they respected him for doing so. Frank kept his college life separate from his home life. He didn't invite college friends to Churchill Ranch or the house in Lincoln Heights.

As he rode his scooter up the gravel road in late May of his freshman year, he could see his father waiting for him. Turridu was wearing a long, moth-eaten coat, probably a hand-me-down from his own father. It flapped in the wind. Frank thought back to his first sighting of the Statue of Liberty. His six-year-old cheek had lain on the scratchy shoulder of that coat. Turridu was older now, slightly stooped. But Frank could see that managing the ranch was good for him.

Frank was bursting with things to tell his father about: Professor Judy's lecture on Emerson; the newly built Mount Wilson Observatory, which he had visited; and midnight jam sessions on evenings when he was able to take off work. Frank had become especially enamored of the poems of Alfred Noyes. "The Highwayman" in particular, one of Noyes's most famous narrative poems, had stirred him deeply. Frank wanted to share all of this with someone, but he felt caught between two worlds: the immigrant boy looking up at the Statue of Liberty, and the young man who was respected by his peers at Throop College of Technology.

"Papà, why do you insist on wearing that moth-eaten old coat?" Frank teased as he parked his scooter.

"It was my papà's coat," Turridu replied. "It makes me

feel like my papà's arms are around me. And the moths are no dummies. They know a good thing. It still keeps me warm and that's what matters. It smells like Bisacquino to me."

"It probably smells like something else," said Frank, smiling.

"Frankie," his father said, suddenly serious, "you're not coming home every night. Where are you staying?"

"I work nights, Papà. Sometimes I stay in the dorm at Throop with friends so I don't have to ride back in the dark."

Satisfied, Turridu changed the subject. "What do you think of this war they got going, Frankie? The war in the old country?" Frank rubbed his chin and said, "I think America will get involved. And at Throop, we are developing all kinds of things to help win the war. I am working on a kind of gas that will penetrate . . . ." Frank trailed off when he realized that his father's attention had drifted away. He was looking out toward the lemon grove.

"I have developed a new way to graft with a T-bud," Turridu said proudly. "Come and look at the rootstock." He walked down the porch steps and Frank followed. "See?" he said, showing Frank a thin branch. "You take the leaves and thorns away, cut an upside-down T, peel back the bark, and insert the bud under the bark. Wrap it safely with tape. That's how you grow things, Frankie. From the root. Then you protect them until they can grow on their own. Like children, eh, Frankie?"

"Yes, Papà," agreed Frank. They walked into the orchard in the deepening twilight.

"I've won a prize, Papà," Frank announced. "The freshman travel prize for getting the highest grades in the class. I get to travel this summer to the University of Chicago, to Massachusetts Institute of Technology, and to the Eastman Kodak Company in Rochester, New York, to see how they produce film."

"Just so you aren't going back to the old country and the wars," replied Turridu. "I don't know all those places. But they sound fancy and important. I respect what you are doing, Frankie. I don't understand any of it. I'm just a simple old man. But I respect it."

Frank did travel that summer to Chicago, Cambridge, Massachusetts, and Rochester. He also spent time in New York City, where he was astounded by the disparity between the poor and the rich. He tried to picture himself riding in a cart through the streets of the Lower East Side. He walked to Battery Park and gazed at the Statue of Liberty in New York Harbor. He vividly recalled looking up at her torch with his father's arms around him. In America, the Capras had not found streets paved with gold. But their hope had been repaid by something else. Here he was, on a trip he had won because he had the highest grades as a freshman at Throop. A Capra at college. Who could have imagined that when they landed?

Frank was especially fascinated by his trip to Eastman Kodak. He learned how film stock is made and encountered the work of early film pioneers Georges Méliès and the Lumière brothers. Frank was impressed by the philanthropy of George Eastman, the founder of the company. He viewed the first moving images of the war in Europe and was mesmerized by the faces of the soldiers, many of whom were exactly his age. The images were silent but immensely powerful. Seeing soldiers moving about in the rain-soaked trenches, doing everyday activities while preparing for brutal battles and smiling at the camera despite horrific conditions, moved Frank to tears.

Frank returned to Throop for his second year tasked with giving two speeches about his summer trip. He wrote out copious notes and arranged for his friend Bob Sticht to show accompanying photographs. But nerves overtook him. He stumbled when walking to the stage, and his meticulously arranged notecards flew everywhere. He had to speak extemporaneously. The students laughed and then grew bored, yawning and shifting as Frank droned on. A kindly professor finally stepped onstage to rescue him.

Bob Sticht approached him after the first speech. "You are doing a second speech tonight, right?"

"Yes, if I don't go out and shoot myself first," said Frank.

"Just tell a few stories," Sticht suggested. "Like you do when we're all together in the dorm in the evenings. You make us all laugh; you put us right inside it all. People don't want to hear facts about the rich and poor in New York City. They want stories. Emotions. Relationships. And, by the way, I need a roommate, and you need to stop wasting your time driving to Churchill Ranch every day. Cap and Sticht. Our room will be the fun way station at Throop."

The idea of living for the first time away from the pressures and tensions of home thrilled Frank. He felt slightly guilty, but he couldn't deny it. With a few extra hours on his shift waiting tables in the Throop dining room, he thought he could afford it.

Like Frank, Bob Sticht was an outsider. He was from Tasmania and he had a funny accent. He had more money than Frank; almost everyone at Throop did. But Stitcht always spoke and behaved in a way that included Frank. He was sensitive to Frank's penury, and it never seemed to get in the way of having fun.

Buoyed by the thought of a new living situation and cognizant of Sticht's advice, Frank entered the Throop auditorium for his second speech with confidence. The professor who introduced him surreptitiously pointed to his watch, implying "Keep it short." But this was a different Frank Capra. He began by saying, "The first time this guy saw Lady Liberty, I was a six-year-old immigrant looking up from my sickbed." He finished with a description of seeing the moving images of British soldiers in trenches.

The audience was captivated and gave him a standing ovation. The next day, Frank moved another step toward independence from his family and moved in with Bob Sticht.

Sticht had a lively, intact family in Pasadena and often invited Frank for dinner at their house. Frank got to know and love the whole family, especially Bob's younger brother, Chet, who eventually became Frank's assistant, working with him for thirty-nine years.

Frank continued to thrill to Clinton Kelly Judy's lectures. He began to write his own poetry and stories. He also took classes in chemical engineering, German, and French. He attended parties and dances and spent time working as a spear-carrier in productions at the Pasadena Playhouse. He loved the atmosphere in the theater and especially the actors. There was a kindness, an acceptance, a sort of joie de vivre that he found exhilarating. He was moved and uplifted by the actors and their dedication to their work. Friends on campus affectionately called him "Cap."

On Friday evening, November 17, 1916, when Frank was in the middle of his second year at Throop, his brother Tony begged him to attend an evening party at Churchill Ranch. "The whole family will be there. Neighbors from Lincoln Heights. Old friends. We never see you. Are you getting to be too good for us, college boy?"

There were a million things Frank would rather have been doing. But as he made his way up the rocky road toward the grove of lemon trees, he could see that Turridu had strung lights and brought tables outside. His father had set up a party, just as if it were Bisacquino. There were plates of pasta con le sarde, caponata, and Sarrida's almond cake. Turridu sat strumming his guitar and singing one of his favorite songs, "Si Maritau Rosa." It was a melancholy song about a young woman, Rosa, who can't get married even though her heart is burning with love.

Ben and his wife Mary were there, and little Sam, who swayed to the music. Tony and Anne were also there, and neighbors from Lincoln Heights who had come to enjoy the party. They sat at the long table together, enjoying the late fall twilight. Turridu wore his long coat to ward off the chill coming down from the San Gabriels. He gave Frank a ukulele, urging him to play along.

"See, it's beautiful out here with the sunset, food, a party, and music. What more do you need in life, eh?" said Turridu, grinning.

"Money. That's what you need in life," said Sarrida with a loud finality. "That is something we never have. Money to pay the bills. Do you think it's going to grow on these lemon trees? Who is paying for this party?"

The argument began. It never really ended. It was a patter in the Capras' lives, a part of how they communicated. Frank wanted nothing more than to be back at Throop with his friends. He quickly kissed his papà. His mother squeezed his cheek and told him to take some food with him. Frank walked quickly to his scooter and began wheeling it down the hill. He looked over his shoulder and saw his father in the fading sunlight, wearing his coat, playing his guitar, and dancing as he sang "Ciuri Ciuri," a popular Sicilian folk song: "Flowers, flowers all the year. The love you gave me, I give you back." Turridu's voice echoed down the hill until it was drowned out by the rumble of the scooter.

The party continued until the early morning hours. When the last car rolled off in clouds of dust, Salvatore Capra looked out over the darkness that enveloped the hills. Stars twinkled in the night sky and he could feel the dryness in the air. Tomorrow morning, he would have to check on the pump house in the orchard to make sure his beloved fruit trees were getting water.

He slept fitfully and awoke with the sunrise. Sam was already awake, eating a slice of bread from the loaves his mother had just baked. Turridu put on his long coat, snatched a loaf of the fragrant bread, and took his grandson's hand.

"Walk with me through the orchard," he said. "What can top a California morning, the smell of lemons and a loaf of fresh bread? Come on. We'll eat while we walk. The Santa Ana winds are here with their dry heat. The trees need water. Just like you, they get thirsty."

The two walked hand-in-hand until they were enveloped in the fragrant lemon trees. They tore off hunks of the fresh bread and stuffed them into their mouths, inhaling the aroma. Turridu's long coat flapped in the wind. As they neared the pump house for the orchard, Turridu heard a strange sound. He let go of his grandson's hand.

"Stay out here for a moment, little one. Your mother doesn't want you in there with those huge gears. I'll be right back. I'm taking the bread," he said with a wink. "I don't trust you with it; you'll eat it all up. And bread is life!" Then he disappeared inside the pump house.

After a brief moment, Sam heard a scream. At first, he thought it was an eagle overhead. Then he realized it was coming from the pump house. It continued without stopping and grew in intensity. There was a grinding sound and then a low, piercing thrum. The five-year-old was terrified. He ran into the orchard with his hands over his ears and hid beneath a lemon tree.

Anne Capra had stayed overnight at the ranch and awoke early to water the roses Turridu had planted in front of the house. She heard an unearthly sound coming from the orchard and ran to investigate. She reached the pump house, forced open the door, and saw her father's body enmeshed between the two huge gears of the water pump. His coat had gotten caught in the gears and dragged him into the machinery. There was blood everywhere. His scream was now a whimper.

It took a moment for Anne's eyes to fully adjust to the darkness of the pump house from the brightness of the early morning. She saw Turridu take his final breath, a rasping gasp. His head hung on his chest. He still clutched the half-eaten loaf of bread in one hand. His body had stopped the motion of one of the gears. The other was chugging around and around.

Anne screamed until she had no voice left. Ben and Mary heard her and came running from the house. Ben was able to stop the motion of the second gear. He removed his father's body from the machinery and laid him on the cement floor of the pump house. Turridu had been cut nearly in two. Anne staggered outside and suffered a minor heart attack. She slumped against one of the young lemon trees.

Frank was at his usual Sunday morning waiter job in the Throop cafeteria. He had more than done his duty to his family last night, he thought, and once all the dishes were cleared away, he had a free day to read and study. He relished the thought. He was surprised to see his favorite professor, Clinton Kelly Judy, rushing toward him.

"Frank! There has been a terrible accident in your family. You need to go to Churchill Ranch immediately! That is the message I was asked to give you." Professor Judy's face was drawn with concern, "Is that your home? Do you want me to take you there?"

Frank didn't want anyone to see his home, which really wasn't his home, or his family. "No, thank you, sir. I'll get myself there." He assumed his parents had had a terrible fight and Ben was calling him to resolve it.

The scene Frank found on arrival at the ranch was one of pure agony. Ben met him, ashen-faced, as Frank drove up the road leading to the orchard. He led him wordlessly toward the pump house. The table from the night before still sat in the middle of the orchard. Ben stopped outside the door to the pump house and said simply, "He is gone, Frank." Frank could hear a wail coming from inside.

He entered to see his mother rocking back and forth, enveloped in grief so raw and uncontained that it filled the room with suffering. The sheer pain of it hit Frank like a sledgehammer. His father's body was covered with the white linen tablecloth that had been on the table during the party the night before. Blood lay in pools. A loaf of bread sat on his chest. Frank stooped to look at his father's face. He immediately wished he hadn't. It was twisted in a look of tortured fright. He would never forget it as long as he lived.

Frank stood up. He showed no outward sign of grief. He took charge, first of his ailing sister, Anne. He found Sam in the orchard and comforted him. He knelt next to his mother and said nothing. He put his arms around her, something he had never done before. When the medical examiner came to take the body, her wail began again, and she had to be forcibly restrained from covering her husband's body with her own.

Sarrida had fought with Turridu often. There were times when she had even despised him. She resented his lack of practicality and loved him for it at the same time. He was the father of her children, the man who had brought music and beauty to their lives in the form of nature. His death left a hole in the family that nothing could fill.

An already fragile Anne became more delicate after the heart attack she suffered that day. In the wake of the tragedy, Ben made a rash decision to let go of the management of Churchill Ranch. Frank tried to reverse the decision with the owners, but the idyllic situation was lost to Ben and his family. They had to return to living in the city.

Sarrida grieved but put away her black widows' clothes after a year, something she would never have done in the old country. She retained her job at the olive oil factory, and the camaraderie of the other women who worked there sustained her. The light Turridu brought to their lives never returned.

Frank was determined to go back to Throop and continue to succeed. But tuition payments became harder to make. The constant financial pressure, combined with the burden of grief, distracted the once promising young student. His grades fell, especially in science, once his best subject.

When America entered into the first World War in 1917, the mood at Throop changed. The young men at Throop felt the need to look outside themselves and their own goals and serve their country. Frank was especially eager to prove his loyalty to America. He signed up for ROTC and discovered, to his surprise and humiliation, that he was not a citizen. (He would become a naturalized citizen in 1920. At that time, he would officially change his name to Frank Russell Capra.)

Frank continued to work furiously, having added ROTC to his already crowded schedule. The one joyous moment happened at a holiday dance during his junior year. Bob Sticht, noting his roommate's struggles, convinced Frank to come out to a Christmas dance, even though Frank was dog-tired from working an overnight shift at Western Pipe and Steel. Sticht loaned him a suit jacket, as Frank's had literally disintegrated. It hung on Frank's compact frame. But his handsome countenance brightened as the two drove down Fair Oaks Boulevard toward Hotel Green, the site of the dance. It had been so long since Frank had done anything just for fun. As they walked under the holly-bedecked archway of the ballroom, waves of perfume and gales of laughter rolled over him. The band was playing a snappy version of the Arthur Fields song "He's Got a Bungalow." Frank forgot his troubles for once.

He was drawn to a petite blonde girl wearing a pink taffeta dress with black velvet trim. She was telling a joke to a mixed group who laughed uproariously. She turned her head and met Frank's gaze with a friendly wink. Frank was amazed when she walked over, held out her hand, and said, "I'm Isabelle Daniels, and none of these lunks can dance to something fast."

"I'm Frank Capra, and you can bet I can," he said without hesitation.

He took her hand. It felt warm. They did a foxtrot and then a one-step.

"Where did you get your sense of rhythm, Mr. Frank Capra?" asked Isabelle.

"From playing the ukulele at the bars on Central Avenue," Frank replied.

He was telling the truth and he was shocked at himself. Something about this girl made him feel it was all right to be honest. There was acceptance, not judgment, in her eyes, and he felt he could tell her anything. They spent the rest of the evening talking. Isabelle invited him for dinner the following weekend. "Five-twenty Madison, seven p.m., and don't be late," she said, "Papa is a stickler for time."

The following Sunday found Frank walking the streets of South Pasadena at 6:00 p.m. He was afraid of being late. He had gotten to the neighborhood an hour early. It was filled with stately brick and stone houses fronted by wide porches and surrounded by white picket fences. He had used manicure scissors to cut the frayed ends from the cuffs of his shirt. He had bought a bouquet of pansies to give to the hostess, but when he stepped onto the porch at precisely 7:00 p.m. and saw the massive flower arrangements in the hallway through the etched glass doors, he quickly threw them into the bushes.

Mr. Daniels answered the door. He was tall and fair-haired. Not a strand was out of place. He wore gold-rimmed glasses over piercing blue eyes that seemed to bore into Frank's with an icy stare.

Isabelle ran down the stairs and was as lively and warm as she had been at the dance. "Papa, did you meet Frank?" she asked.

"Yes, I did," he said, although he hadn't yet said a word to him. "Let's go in to dinner."

His tone made it known that this was something he wanted to dispense with as soon as possible. Mr. Daniels slid open pocket doors to reveal a long, lace-covered table. A woman stood at one end. She had Isabelle's warm smile.

"Welcome, Frank," Mrs. Daniels said. "I am Isabelle's mother. She has told me all about you."

The dinner was awkward, despite Isabelle's efforts to keep the conversation afloat. Mr. Daniels maintained a stony silence. At one point, Frank realized he needed to use the restroom but didn't know how to ask politely. Finally, Isabelle saw him beginning to stand and said, "The powder room is at the end of the hall." Frank had never heard the term "powder room" but followed her directions. He found the toilet and two delicate lace-trimmed towels hanging near the sink. He couldn't imagine wiping his hands on them, so he used his pant leg. He was walking back down the hall when he heard loud voices. Mr. Daniels's boomed out.

"This is what comes of allowing Isabelle to go anywhere, do anything. She's brought home an Italian. A wop. A dago!"

The insulting words were like punches to Frank's gut. He froze. Suddenly he hated, with all of his being, the deep soft carpet, the immaculate wainscoting, the etched glass doors at the end of the hallway. He despised all the symbols of wealth and privilege. He hated people who saw people like his family as threats to their staid existence. Frank wanted nothing more than to slam out the front door. But he wasn't going to give them that. He was not going to run away.

"Papa, those are horrible words," Isabelle was saying. "Frank is one of the smartest and most polite boys I have ever met."

"Don't speak to your father that way, Isabelle," said Mrs. Daniels. "I won't allow rudeness in my home."

Frank entered the room. He walked to his place and picked up his napkin as if to sit down. Then he stood up straight and said, "I have studies at Throop which make it imperative for me to return there at once. Thank you for your hospitality."

He turned on his heel and stalked out of the house. He closed the front door with a finality that made the etched glass shake. He was five blocks down California Boulevard before he realized he was still clutching a dinner napkin with the monogram D, probably a wedding gift. He folded it neatly and kept it in his pocket. He felt it there for days. It was a symbol. A reminder. He would never allow anyone to treat him like that again.

Isabelle apologized, of course, in her forthright manner. "You are my friend. We are the new generation, and those things don't matter to us. I hate him. I hate that he thinks like that and speaks like that."

To Frank, the worst part of her apology was the word "friend." He didn't want to be her friend. He wanted to be much more.

The war put a damper over the Throop graduating class of

1918. Almost all the graduates were bound for military service, among them Frank Capra. He received his commission at graduation time. He would not be on a troop transport going to the heart of the battle. He was instead assigned to teach math to ballistics experts at an army training center in San Francisco. Many of the graduates had already been in service, like Frank, during their final years at Throop. The celebratory feeling of graduation was leavened, especially for loved ones who were worried about the dangers that lay ahead for their sons.

Ben and Mary were unable to come. Tony had to work. But Sarrida, dressed in her finest, and Anne, still pale and thin but grinning with joy for her brother, came hours early so they could sit in the front row. As Frank stepped off the stage with his diploma, Sarrida burst into tears, saying, "Your Papà would have been so proud!"

Frank could hear the slap of cards on the kitchen table. Sarrida and three friends from the C. P. Grogan olive oil factory were playing Scopa. They had a regular Thursday night game. They all met around the rickety wooden table in Sarrida's kitchen because she made the best lasagna. They had shared joys, tears, and many laughs over endless hands of cards for more than a decade.

"What's wrong with your Frankie?" asked Lydia, Sarrida's best friend and fiercest competitor. "Where the hell is he?"

"He's sleeping in the next room. He's sick. Keep your voice down," said Sarrida.

"With what? Too much reading?" replied Lydia. This got a laugh from the other women.

"It's some sort of stomach illness," Sarrida said. "He had that terrible Spanish flu when he was in the army. I've been coming home every day at lunch to put raw potatoes on his forehead. By the way, I won this round."

"Didn't he go to that fancy college? I thought you said he was gonna be a bank president. Seems to me like he's President Freeloader," said Lydia. More laughter. "Oh, Sarrida, I'm just joking. Maybe Frank can join us down at the olive oil factory. He can read the labels to us!"

Frank was mortified. He writhed in pain in the airless bedroom of his mother's apartment. He had received a medical discharge shortly after the Armistice, then been confined to bed with a horrible, unrelenting ache in his stomach. Sarrida didn't believe in doctors and tried home remedies. Nothing quelled the stabbing pain. But that night, he determined he would leave his mother's apartment, no matter how miserable he felt, if it was the last thing he did.

It was the morning of the New Year, 1919. Frank staggered to the trolley on Sunset Boulevard as the pink sky faded to blue over Union Station. He wore his army uniform. It was the only thing he had that was clean. He boarded the trolley bound for his brother Ben's house in Van Nuys. Anything would be better than listening to Sarrida's cackling friends. Ben and Mary welcomed him into their home, but Frank insisted on sleeping in a hammock that he fashioned in the backyard. He rigged up a small shed that he used as an office and began to write stories.

He alternated writing, during the next several weeks, with resting in the hammock. He pondered what to do with his life. As he lay in the hammock and looked up at the sky, his pain began to subside. One day in March, Mary came running outside with a clipping from the newspaper. "It's an ad, Frank. For a tutor. In Arcadia. I think it would be perfect for you."

The following afternoon, Frank looked up at the massive double doors of the Baldwin estate in Arcadia. It was at the corner of Baldwin Avenue and Foothill Boulevard. Letters on the wrought iron archway spelled out ANOAKIA, which Frank presumed was the name of the property. There were balustrades, turrets, several wide porches, and three stories that he could see. The yard had been landscaped with fountains, velvety green grass, and cement statuary.

Frank walked up a set of marble stairs that led to a terrace with more marble stairs. Standing under a black-and-white striped awning, he rang a doorbell the size of a dinner plate. The door was answered by a butler in full uniform. He ushered Frank into a solarium that was tiled with an artist's interpretation of scenes from Native American life. Several stuffed peacocks stood so realistically that Frank reached out to touch one to see if it would move.

"My father was obsessed with peacocks . . . well, he was obsessed with money first, then women, then peacocks," said a voice directly behind him.

Frank turned to see a tall, dark-haired woman with enormous, searching eyes. He put out his hand to shake hers, but she took his hand in both of hers.

"The day after he died, when they read the will, I tore down everything he said not to tear down and I built this place. All of it. I'm Anita Baldwin. I'm the daughter of Lucky Baldwin. I will get right to the point, Fred."

"It's Frank, ma'am," said Frank.

"Frank, then. Are you Italian?" she asked, then added, without waiting for an answer, "I don't care what you are. You have to save my son. He's turning into a profligate cretin with all of my father's bad habits and none of his luck. He's got to get into college, and I am not going to pay off the University of Southern California, though I could, to pave the way. He has to do it himself. He needs to learn to do something besides drinking and gambling. You look intelligent, Fred. I like you already. Fate has sent you to me. I believe in fate, don't you? You are the Capra fellow, right? The fellow applying for a job as a tutor and not the fellow interviewing for the gardener job?"

Frank jumped in, as he felt she would go on forever unless he did. "I am Frank Capra," he said. "I am an American citizen. And I can save your son. I can make sure he enters USC or wherever he wants to go in the fall. You have my word."

"Sit down, young man," she said, leading him to a chaise lounge, "I want to hear every word about you."

Frank wondered what to tell her, but he needn't have worried. Anita Baldwin talked about herself for the next hour. She described her childhood in San Francisco, the four marriages of her father, moving to the rancho in Arcadia as a child, her father's near death when a mistress took a shot at him.

"She missed, you see," Anita Baldwin explained. "He was lucky then, lucky when he sold whiskey to fellow travelers on the Oregon Trail when he first came west, lucky when he told his servant to sell all his shares of silver mines and then left for Europe. The servant couldn't find the key to his safe, didn't sell the shares, and they quadrupled in value. That's how he got his name. He owns 47,000 acres of land around here. Or owned. Until he died. Now I've inherited lots of his money. My mother was his third and favorite wife. The pretty one. You can tell because there are portraits of her all around the house. My own children are simply a trial. And it has been sheer hell to try to build this house, find the decorators, order the porcelain, hire over fifty servants. I tell you, Fred, I'm exhausted. So exhausted. I have worked my fingers to the bone."

Frank glanced at her long, tapered ivory fingers. They were covered with diamond rings. He thought of Sarrida's brown, gnarled fingers with nails permanently yellowed from the glue on the olive oil labels.

"My son is late, as usual," Anita Baldwin said. "Let me take you on a tour."

A walk through the grounds revealed live peacocks and stables housing racehorses. Inside the house, Frank lost track of the number of rooms and hallways. When they entered an oak-paneled library filled with books, he gasped. He carefully picked up a Ralph Waldo Emerson from a table. "Is this a first edition?" he asked, astonished.

"A first what?" answered Anita. "Heavens, I have no idea. No one here ever reads. It was just filled in by a decorator. You can borrow anything you like and come here anytime, if that's what suits you. I'd recommend the pool, though. You will be alone in this room, dear. No one ever comes into the library." She gave a silvery laugh.

A lithe blond young man dressed in tennis whites came loping into the room. He was swinging a tennis racquet. "So sorry to be late. But I had to finish the match." He held out his hand to Frank. "Baldwin Baldwin," the young man said. "It used to be something else. But Mum changed it to Baldwin after the nasty divorce. You must be the person she's hired to beat me into submission. You'll never do that, but we can have a grand time together anyhow." He had the energy of a puppy.

Frank saw a steely side to Anita Baldwin when she addressed her son. "I am serious. Fred here, or Frank, is going to give you a test each week. If you fail, you won't get your allowance." It sounded to Frank like a mother addressing an unruly toddler. Then the two started discussing an upcoming trip and the purchase of a new racehorse. It was as though Frank was not even there.

Finally, Anita Baldwin turned to Frank and said, "Darling, we must be boring you to tears. Come back tomorrow at noon, when Baldwin finally wakes up, and start the hardest job in the world? I'll leave a bottle of aspirin in the library. You'll need it."

Anita Baldwin was not far wrong. Frank spent the spring and summer of 1919 working, or attempting to work, with Baldwin. The goal was clear: The young man had to pass the entrance exam for the University of Southern California. Anita Baldwin could easily have bought his way in with a large donation, but she remained adamant that he would earn his acceptance.

One night, in exchange for a full day of study, Frank agreed to go out on the town with Baldwin, who conveniently forgot his wallet. They went from bar to bar on Central Avenue, to haunts in Angelino Heights, and to gambling dens on Sunset Boulevard not far from where Frank lived when he first came to America. They ended the night sipping from a flask Baldwin produced from the glove compartment of his car. They were parked on a hill near the stables at Anoakia, and the soft whinnying of the horses punctuated their conversation.

"What's the point of it all, right?" said an inebriated Baldwin, "I'm going to inherit millions. I don't need a college education to make more money to enjoy my life. I've already got it all."

Frank turned to him. "You don't want to learn about where you came from, about history? You don't want to understand politics, the country you live in, what it means to be an American? You don't want to know about other people, how they live, what they think, what makes them tick? You don't care about people's lives, their stories, what is important to them?"

Baldwin smiled like a Cheshire cat. "Listen, Frankie boy, all that stuff is for saps who can't do any better for themselves." He brandished his flask and patted his own chest. "These are my values. Look out for Number One. If it makes me comfortable and I like it, it's good. If it doesn't, it's bad. That's my motto. All the rest is hogwash. I'm telling it like it is, Frankie boy."

Frank felt himself growing furious. It took every ounce of self-control not to lash out at Baldwin. But tomorrow, Baldwin would take the entrance exam. If he passed, Frank would get a bonus he could give to Sarrida. The rest he had saved. He was ready to get out of Arcadia, out of Pasadena, out of Los Angeles. He wanted to explore the real world, to find his own calling.

Baldwin narrowly passed the exam, and his mother put together an impromptu dinner party to celebrate. They invited Frank. He spent the evening at a long table covered with damask, eating from Limoges china and surrounded by some of the most wealthy and powerful people in Los Angeles. They came to pay homage to Anita Baldwin, although Frank could tell it was only to secure connections to her money. Frank was no longer intimidated. He knew what spoon to use and how to fold his napkin. He had spent hours in the sun-drenched library at Anoakia. His favorite times that summer were sitting in the leather chair in front of the picture window, reading.

He gazed around at his dinner companions. They were engaged in conversations about which ski resorts in Switzerland had the best food and how to manage "those infernal, lazy servants." The stress of having to design their own jewelry because nothing at the stores was "right." He found their conversation vapid and boring. He was glad to excuse himself at the end of the evening.

Anita Baldwin was quite drunk. She grabbed his hand in hers, as she had done on the first day. One of her diamonds caught the sleeve of his well-worn shirt and ripped a hole in the sleeve. "What will we do without our darling Frankie? I will replace this shirt with ten new ones, dear. You could use them anyway. This one is a rag. Good-bye, dear. We simply adore you."

Frank was relieved to walk down the marble steps of Anoakia for the last time. He'd had his fill of rich people. The night air calmed him as he drove toward the city of Los Angeles. He passed the turn-off for Churchill Ranch and thought of his father. A feeling of pride swelled within him: pride for the hard work and resilience of his mother, for the hope and love of his father. He vowed to live a life that would honor them. A life that would inspire others.

Anita Baldwin did not send him ten shirts. She did not send him even one shirt. Frank was not surprised. He patched the one she had torn and wore it for the next ten years.

Chapter Three

THE EMBRACE OF CREATIVITY

"Are you sure you can wrangle this horse?" asked Coney, the pug-nosed cowboy. He pulled at the reins of a skittish roan. "If this filly wrecks his shot, the director will scream at you 'til he's blue in the face. You say you worked with horses before, right, kid?"

The sun beat down, and Frank had to squint to see. "Oh, yes, sir. I know all about horses."

He was lying, of course. He'd seen Baldwin handle horses at Anoakia and mounted police in downtown Los Angeles. He'd seen horses running at Santa Anita. But he had never even touched a rein himself. Now it was his job to prepare the horse before the star of the film jumped onto it for the climactic scene. The job paid. And Frank was desperate for the cash.

"Well, I guess I believe you," said Coney. "And we are short of hands, so I got no choice. You'd better get yourself a hat. With that pale skin, you're gonna burn to a crisp. You Italian? Name sounds Italian. Never seen no Italian wrangle a horse." He threw the reins to Frank. "Here. Brush 'er down. I got a hundred things to do before the crew shows up."

Frank had happened on the set while visiting his brother Ben, who had moved with his family to Sacramento. It was July of 1921. Frank was in downtown Sacramento when he noticed the chaos and the swirl of activity. He was fascinated. The voice of a young John Ford, the director, echoed through the streets. Frank watched the precision with which Ford set up his shot, which involved a deadly encounter between two rival gunmen, and took note of the way he spoke to both of his actors. Frank had approached Coney and asked if they needed someone.

At 5:00 a.m. the following day, Frank was on set calming Flossie, the horse, and awaiting the arrival of the star of the film, Harry Carey. Frank shaded his eyes and looked down the road, expecting the star to arrive in a chauffeured limousine. Flossie was bucking and pulling.

"Kid, don't hold the reins like that," said a voice in the pre-dawn darkness. "She doesn't like it. You look like a green-horn to me. I've been on this earth for thirty-two years and I know a greenhorn when I see one. You ever been on a film set before, sonny?"

With a shock, Frank recognized the tall, rangy man as Carey. He had seen that face on countless posters plastered around Los Angeles. Now he was standing in front of him on a deserted road ten miles south of Sacramento.

"What's your name, kid? Where are you from?" asked Carey, crossing his arms and staring intently at Frank.

"Frank Capra, sir. Italy, then Los Angeles and then Throop." Frank put out his hand.

Harry Carey shook it and whistled through his teeth. "I went to Hamilton College and then NYU," the actor said. "I wanted to be a lawyer, but I got bit by the film bug. You want to be in show business, kid? You want to make movies?" Harry asked, patting Flossie.

"Yes, sir," said Frank without hesitation, surprising even himself.

In his back pocket, he carried a letter from his former high school teacher, Rob Wagner, who now published a film magazine in Los Angeles. Frank had written to Rob for advice about whether he should try the film business. Wagner had insisted that Frank pursue science and think of film as a hobby. He outlined the uncertainty, the insecurity, and the difficulty of the movie business and encouraged Frank to continue on the road of engineering. He concluded his letter urging Frank to abandon any notion of making a career in film.

"You've made the best decision ever," Harry Carey was saying. "I'm telling you, kid, this is the best life you can imagine. In what other job could I be standing here with a cup of coffee at sunrise on a beautiful day talking with a smart young college man and spending my hours riding horses? And getting paid for it to boot!"

Over the next two weeks, Frank learned to handle Flossie. When he couldn't, Harry was glad to give him tips. There was only one day when Ford blew up at Frank because he failed to get out of a shot. It never happened again. Ford's blow-ups were common. Frank understood the reasons for them, but he also took note of how they upset the cast and crew. He decided that if he ever got the chance to direct, he would keep his temper in check no matter what happened.

Time turned inside out when they began night shoots. Eager to learn about all aspects of filmmaking, Frank made himself available to the gaffers and grips. He organized the prop wagon, hauled equipment, and made sure there was hot coffee ready when the crew showed up at dawn. He endeared himself to everyone during the three-week shoot, but most particularly to Harry Carey and his new wife, Olive, who was with her husband on location. They had long talks between takes, sitting under ancient pepper trees on equipment barrels.

Frank told Harry about the past three years of his life. He had spent part of that time wandering the West, peddling Elbert Hubbard's books door-to-door. "I sat down at the kitchen tables of farm families and talked to crowds at county fairs," Frank said. "Even though I sometimes found it hard to convince people to buy, I never doubted the subject matter. It was inspirational. Hubbard believed in hard work, efficiency, perseverance. He believed in salvation through economic, social, and spiritual freedom."

"See, this stuff is gold!" said Harry. "The people, the stories, the feelings they evoke. This is what you'll use in your work. It's gold, I tell you. They'll never get to my shot before the end of the day. Why don't you come back to the hotel with Olive and me and have dinner. I want to hear more of your stories. All I have to talk about is film sets. You've lived real life."

At Frasinetti's Winery and Restaurant in Sacramento that night, Carey asked Frank for more stories about his life going door-to-door. Frank took a bite of filet mignon and warmed to his subject.

"Well, there is nothing like being invited in at, say, supper-time, on a farm outside Acton," he began. "You are a novelty, see, and maybe they haven't seen anyone new in months. And you tell them about Elbert Hubbard and how he started his own business and his belief that there is no such thing as genius, just the power of making continuous efforts . . . or, to put it another way, that a genius is simply someone who takes the lemons life has given him and starts a lemonade stand. That gets to me every time and I agree with it. I believe it."

"If that isn't the truth," agreed Harry. "Have you got any of those books left?"

"Oh, no," said Frank emphatically. "My door-to-door days are over. I'm pursuing a life in the movies."

Harry slapped the table and ordered three whiskeys, neat. "We've gotta celebrate, son. You'll never regret it. Ford's the real deal. You got to start with the best. I think you're going to go places, kid. I'm wrapped, so I won't see you tomorrow."

"Wrapped?" asked Frank, confused.

"It means done. *Fini*. Over. I'm taking my wife Olive and heading to the next circus. And I love every minute of it. Long as I'm working, it's okay with me. Best life ever." Harry said.

When the waitress arrived, he threw back his shot of whiskey and ordered another round.

Frank arrived on location at 5:00 a.m. the next day, slightly hungover. He was shocked to find empty spaces where, for the past three weeks, there had been long tables full of actors and crew members eating, drinking coffee, and chatting. Frank gave Flossie one last brush-down, made sure she was fed, and saw her loaded into a rickety truck. Her tail swished as the truck pulled out in a cloud of dust. Soon, there was nothing left.

"The circus has moved off, Sonny," said Coney. "That's why they call 'em movies. 'Cause they move." He handed Frank a business card. "Harry said to give this to you. Said you could use it if you want to. He can't vouch for the company personally, but he said you could see if they are legit."

The front was printed with "Tri-State Films, Reno, Nevada, W. M. Planck." On the back, Carey had scrawled, "Don't know this guy, but heard they are hiring. Good luck, kid. See ya in the movies." It was signed "Harry Carey."

Planck was indeed a producer, of sorts, with a girlfriend named Ida Heitman. Frank sought them out in Reno and they hired him, on the basis of his college education, to be a treasurer and producer for their fledgling film production company. Frank was put up in a sketchy hotel in Reno. He contracted gonorrhea and went to a local hack doctor for treatment. The doctor gave him a botched circumcision that would affect him for the rest of his life.

After the operation, Frank lay in pain at the hotel for three days. He stared up at the crumbling ceiling. It was 1922 and he was twenty-five years old. The physical pain matched the ache in his soul. He thought of Isabelle Daniels, as he always did in moments of loneliness. He had written to her often during the past few years and she always replied. Frank was grateful. In her letters, she was exactly the same as she was in person. They shared details of their lives and thoughts and feelings. It was the one strong connection Frank had to home.

Now Frank took out a sheet of paper and described to Isabelle the whole sordid experience in Reno. He described the seedy feeling of the town, his doubts about Tri-State Films, and his sense of isolation. He detailed the shame and regret he now felt. He ended the letter by saying that he hoped his confession, and the honesty it represented, would draw them closer. He wrote that he realized he needed Isabelle. Frank was able to sleep soundly that night for the first time in weeks. He mailed the letter the next morning at the tiny post office in downtown Reno.

Frank waited two agonizing weeks to hear from Isabelle. The first film made by Tri-State had been released and had sunk under the surface with barely a ripple. It was not successful. Frank returned to the Overland at the end of a long week to find two letters. One was from Isabelle. The other was from his brother Tony, who had never written to him before. He eagerly tore into Isabelle's, hoping for the balm of her wisdom and encouragement. Instead he read, with increasing horror, that her father had intercepted Frank's letter. He had told Isabelle that it confirmed every negative thought he'd had about Frank. Furthermore, if Isabelle ever saw Frank again, he would disown her.

In a second, even more devastating paragraph, Isabelle confessed that she was in love with Frank's college friend Bob Griffis and was planning to marry him. She expressed wonder at how falling in love worked, that Bob's touch was electric from the start and that for her, Frank would always be the smartest, most dear and unique person; she was glad to be able to tell him about this new part of her life. She apologized again for her father and hoped that Frank could find it in his heart to be happy for her. She wanted to remain friends always.

Frank staggered to an armchair in the lobby of the Overland. The stuffing was coming out of the seat and the springs were broken. He gazed at the letter. He wanted to find a love like that. He stared out the window. A desert rainstorm was pelting the panes and landing on the dusty street like bullets. Frank stared at the rivulets of water. Memories of Isabelle filled his mind. He couldn't push them away.

Finally, Frank roused himself and opened the letter from Tony. It was brief and to the point. Tony had met a bootlegger from San Francisco who needed an engineer to work on his stills. He was offering $20,000 to someone who could rig the stills so they wouldn't blow up. Tony called it the "chance of a lifetime." He seemed proud of the notion of helping his little brother in this way. He closed by saying, "Don't say I never did nothing for you. Leave this movie stuff behind. It'll never amount to anything. This is real world stuff! Get up to Frisco! Here's $10.

I know you need it." A bill enclosed in the letter floated to the floor.

Frank folded and refolded the money. He tore Isabelle's letter into tiny pieces. He piled up the scraps in a rusty standing ashtray next to his chair. He lit them on fire and watched the flames jump up, then die away. Nothing could burn away the sadness in his heart.

The next day, Frank arrived outside a warehouse near the Embarcadero in San Francisco. He had a meeting with Tony's acquaintance. He'd spoken with him briefly on the phone. The gravelly voice had said, "I'm going to have me a fancy pants college guy fixing my stills. That's what Tony says you are. If you can do this for me boy, you'll go far in this business." It grated on Frank. He stood outside the warehouse at the appointed time. He'd been given a series of instructions on how to get inside, as it was heavily guarded. The $20,000 may as well have been $20 million, he needed it so badly. He could buy a house for Sarrida and a dress shop for Anne. He hesitated.

And in that moment of hesitation, Frank recalled Dr. Scherer's welcoming speech on the first day at Throop. He hadn't thought of it in years. He remembered the hope and inspiration he had felt that day. He thought of his father pointing to the Statue of Liberty, of his mother and the happiness in her eyes on his graduation day. He thought of Rob Wagner and his hopes for each of his students. Frank turned up his threadbare collar and walked away, down Van Ness Avenue. He found a flophouse near the wharves. He could hear the harbor seals barking and the slap of the water against the docks. A couple in the next room was having a loud argument about money. Frank had two dollars to his name.

He woke up the next morning and got on a cable car headed for Golden Gate Park. He needed to clear his head. He had no idea what his future held. It was early in the morning and the car was deserted. A newspaper left by a previous passenger flapped in the wind and landed at his feet. Frank picked it up and glanced through it, searching for the employment section. An advertisement caught his eye: "Wanted: Experienced director for a film based on the work of Rudyard Kipling. Apply to Walter Montague at the Post Stages." The address was not far from the last stop on the cable car line.

Frank looked at himself in the reflection of the window. He hadn't shaved in two days. His curly dark hair stood on end. He licked his palms, ran his hands through his hair and tried to smooth out his wrinkled shirt. He grabbed the cable and signaled for a stop. He walked by a florist who was arranging carnations in a large bucket. One had snapped off. She looked at Frank and offered it to him with a wink. He took it gratefully and put it in his lapel.

The address was another large, inconsequential looking building, but this time Frank did not hesitate. He knocked on the door and a basso voice answered, "If you are here for the interview, do come in."

Frank opened the door, which creaked, and stepped into a nearly empty warehouse. Sunlight poured through a huge picture window, spilling over the figure seated in front. Dust motes created lines of shadow and light. When Frank's eyes adjusted, he saw a large man sitting on a throne-like chair on a raised platform behind a huge wooden desk. He was wearing a velvet tunic and a porkpie hat that perched precariously on the back of his head. The desk was filled with books, stacked and opened and scattered across the surface.

"Come in, come on, come in!" the man boomed, "My name is Walter Montague. You are the first to arrive. Do I have your name on my list?"

"No," said Frank, "we haven't spoken yet. But I saw your advertisement in the paper and I thought I would just come."

"Ahhh . . . an enterprising, risk-taking, gritty young man! I like that. As Shakespeare said, 'Boldness be my friend.'"

"From 'Cymbeline,' one of my favorites," answered Frank.

"Mine too, mine too!" said Montague, almost in tears. "What an amazing young man! I am referring to you. But, of course, to Shakespeare, too."

"My name is Frank Capra."

"Ahhh . . . it has an Italian ring to it! Your ancestors come from the land of Dante, Michelangelo, and da Vinci, not to mention Puccini and the great actress Eleonora Duse. Where are you from, dear boy?" By now, Montague had hoisted himself up and was coming around the desk to shake hands.

Frank swallowed and said, "Hollywood. I am a director from Hollywood." Montague stopped as if electrified. At first Frank wondered if he was having some sort of attack. Montague's eyes bugged out and he clutched his chest.

"Hollywood? Did you say Hollywood? A director?" asked an incredulous Montague.

"Yes. Yes, that's right." Frank had no idea what he would say if asked for his experience.

Montague swept off his hat and executed a surprisingly graceful bow. "Then I kiss your feet. I need look no further. I have found my man. Kismet has sent you to me! Do you know Rudyard Kipling?"

Frank racked his brain for a Kipling quote and remembered one he had learned from Professor Clinton Kelly Judy at Throop. "Not personally," he said, "but I live by his words 'If history were taught in the form of stories, it would never be forgotten.'"

"Not only a director from Hollywood, but an intelligent, learned man!" Montague said. "I am in ecstasy. Our first film will be based on a Kipling poem, 'Fultah Fisher's Boarding House.' It is a dark tale of life lived among those who have to scrape for every morsel and for whom life is nearly every day a tragedy. It is to be moving. Memorable. Human. Authentic. The budget is $1,800. Do you think you can do it?"

Frank didn't hesitate. "Of course I can."

Montague pointed him toward a chair in front of the huge desk, and they spent the rest of the day poring over scenarios and exchanging ideas. Frank found Montague to be intelligent and thoughtful, though woefully ignorant about making movies.

Montague was happy to let Frank take the reins. "I have friends here who have equipment, friends who are editors, and I will introduce you. I see something in you, Frank Capra. We are going to make a beautiful movie."

The sun was setting as Frank and Montague left the studio. Frank had entered it midmorning as a destitute man fending off employment from a bootlegger. He was leaving as a director of his first film. Montague took Frank to Fior d'Italia at the corner of Kearny and Broadway. He encouraged the hungry young man to order steak, pasta, and tiramisu; he could see it had been a long time since Frank had eaten a meal like that. Montague tactfully didn't ask about Frank's past experience. He insisted on paying for the meal and clapped Frank on the shoulder as they parted, saying, "It is my lucky day today."

Frank was certain that Montague expected him to cast the film, find the location, and hire all the technicians and crew. He was eager to do so because he felt confident of his leadership abilities. He walked home that night filled with thoughts about the upcoming work and grateful for the providence that had led him to this kind, joyful man. Frank was determined to repay Montague's faith in him by delivering a product in which he could take pride. He returned to his tiny room at the flophouse. The same couple was arguing about the same thing. But Frank was now too engrossed in his own thoughts to pay any attention to them.

He stayed up the entire night making lists, writing out scenes, and detailing them on sheets of paper that he stuck to the walls of his room. He worked in a frenzy, walking back and forth to pin sheets of paper to the walls. By dawn, they were covered. He had envisioned each scene in detail: a tragic tale set inside a seedy wharf bar whose denizens lived lives filled with pain and difficulty. He wanted this to be reflected in the faces that appeared in the film and thought about hiring actual sailors and prostitutes from the wharves. He wanted to create reality and authenticity.

Frank barely slept for three days. When he began to tire, more exciting possibilities would crop up and adrenalin would start flowing again. He interviewed sailors and realized that while some of them might work as extras, actors brought the ability to be consistent and create emotion within the often challenging technical necessities of repeating scenes. He ended up using a combination of professional and nonprofessional actors. He realized that some of the nonprofessionals would appear in the film without pay, just for the experience.

After three almost sleepless days, Frank collapsed on the floor of his hotel room. Time had gone by in a kaleidoscope of creative thoughts and ideas. He had scoured the wharves and found a location. He had interviewed actresses for the crucial role of Anne of Austria, the proprietress of Fultah Fisher's boarding house. There was some pay. Frank's heart went out to the young women, many with holes in their stockings and patched dresses, who desperately wanted the role. Many were beautiful. Too beautiful. He was looking for someone who had beauty but also a face etched in tragedy, someone who had known poverty and sorrow. He found her in a tiny birdlike actress named Mildred Owen. Her hair was windblown, as if she hadn't brushed it in days, and she was older than the other actresses he had seen. She had a tormented look. Frank hired her on the spot.

Montague had brought the camera equipment to the studio that day. Frank asked Mildred to sit for a moment. He put his camera on the tripod and arranged Mildred in front of Montague's picture window. The late afternoon light was golden. It streamed into the room. Frank looked through the eyepiece and instinctively moved closer until Mildred's haunted face took up the whole frame. His heart began to pound so hard he thought it would burst from his chest. In that face, framed by the camera, he saw yearning, sorrow, beauty, and life. He couldn't wait for tomorrow.

"Thank you, Mildred!" he told her. "Thank you so much. That is just what I needed," said Frank.

"Oh, no, thank *you*, Mr. Director," Mildred said, smiling broadly.

"I was so moved," Frank continued. "If I might ask, what were you thinking about?"

"Ummm . . . getting a big ham sandwich with a pickle," she replied. "I'm so darned hungry!"

Frank had just had his first lesson in directing actors. It didn't matter what they were actually thinking, as long as the story he wanted to tell came across in their eyes, their expressions. But it occurred to him that if all the actors in a scene understood the story they were telling, it might unify the cast and economize the time spent. The camera framed moments of human emotion in such a way that they were enlarged, made indelible and inescapable. Or at least, that is what Frank decided he wanted.

The shoot was thrilling for Frank. His love of the actors and his love of what he was doing transferred to everyone on the set. He saw how informing the cast and crew what they were going for in each scene helped to shape and motivate behavior. It allowed the people working on the scene to invest in the outcome. Frank planned meticulously, going over each shot and expenditure for the next day. *Fultah Fisher's Boarding House* came in at twelve minutes and $100 under budget. Frank book-ended the film with an old man sitting by a fire and reading a book of poems.

Montague was thrilled with the film, and it made a small profit. He was eager to continue collaborating with the resourceful young man. For his part, Frank felt he had been able to make full use of the skills he had honed over the past few years. The scientific aspect of filmmaking appealed to him and excited him. He knew he had a lot more to learn and was deter-mined to do so.

Frank declined Montague's offer of another film. He had already set his sights on other things. He wanted to learn about the process of editing, in particular, and went to work for Walter Bell, an editor of some note in San Francisco who made short films. Frank met Bob Eddy, a producer of short films, through Walter Bell and began to learn the magic of editing. A dog running down the street wasn't funny. But a dog running down the street splashing mud on a pretentious rich snob was hilar-ious. It was all in the setup and ultimately in the editing.

Frank Capra, at the age of twenty-six, felt he had found his life's work. Despite the warnings of Rob Wagner, his former English teacher at Manual Arts, he was mesmerized by the challenge of filmmaking. It occupied his entire being. He still went back to his one-room apartment on Mission Street alone.

In the early summer of 1923, Frank met a niece of one of the producers at Bob Eddy's company. It was a June evening and Eddy had thrown a rooftop party. Frank walked up the stairs to the roof and saw a rail-thin young woman wearing a white sequined dress, sleeveless in the chilly San Francisco night air. Her hair was bobbed. She held a cigarette in a holder in one hand and a martini glass in the other. She was just finishing her drink. She stubbed out her cigarette on the marble balustrade and tossed the butt over the side. She stared out at the Bay and the Golden Gate Bridge. The sun was setting and Alcatraz could be seen in a cloudy haze. She suddenly turned to Frank and said, "The worst thing about Alcatraz would have to be the lack of martinis."

"We're not on Alcatraz," said Frank stepping closer to her, "Can I get you another? I never get martinis for young ladies if I don't know their name."

"You first," she said with a laugh. "What's your name, martini fetcher?"

"Frank. Frank Capra. Are you an actress? You look so familiar."

"What a corny line. Oh, yes, I most certainly am. Let's see . . . Capra . . . does that have any relation to the word capricious?" As she spoke, she was sizing him up and down.

"Impressive. Yes, it does," answered Frank.

"Not all actresses are dumb. And no, I didn't want to be in your silly movie about wharf rats. Yes, I auditioned for you.

Downtrodden waif isn't my wheelhouse, though. And yes, I'll have another. Helen is my name. Helen Howell. I guess I didn't make much of an impression when I auditioned for you."

Frank recovered quickly, saying, "You were far, far too beautiful to be in that film. But I can think of a million others you could star in."

"If you think I'm going to fall for that line, you are absolutely right. Get little Helen a drinky-winky now."

They spent the entire summer together, going to plays at the Curran Theater and seeing every film they could. Helen was from a wealthy theatrical family, and they treated themselves to the best seats. It was Prohibition, but Helen also knew every bar in San Francisco, from the speakeasies in the Tenderloin to the Nob Hill nightclubs. The owners all seemed to know her. She was adept at planning their evenings to coincide with visits to bars at regular intervals. An aspiring actress, she took acting classes, although she missed them frequently because of recovery from her late nights.

Frank and Helen shared one dream: to move to Hollywood. They spoke about it constantly. On Halloween, 1923, they rode the cable car to the top of Nob Hill. It was late in the afternoon and costumed revelers were already making their way down the hill to North Beach parties. Helen was dressed as a Kewpie. She looked adorable to Frank. As they reached the top of Powell Street, Frank turned to Helen and said, "I've got two ideas. Let's move to Hollywood."

"I won't say no to that," Helen responded.

"Let's get married," said Frank.

"In my Kewpie outfit? Please let me change! Oh yes, yes, yes!" Helen threw her arms around him. "Let's celebrate! I know where there is a bottle of champagne on ice!"

Before they left for Hollywood, Frank was hired to direct an Italian documentary about the arrival of an Italian naval warship, the *Libia*, in San Francisco Harbor. *La visita dell'Incrociatore Italiano Libia a San Francisco, Calif.* required an enormous effort of planning, coordination, and execution, as it involved a sequence of events including crowds at the arrival, welcome speeches, and a formal dinner. Frank filmed it all, edited the documentary, and presented it to the delighted committee. He had proved to himself that he had the artistic sensibility and the practical capability needed to make films.

On Thanksgiving Day, 1923, Frank and Helen were married in Helen's apartment in Pacific Heights. When the last guest had left, Helen disappeared from the parlor with a smile and returned wearing a beautiful black lace dressing gown. Frank nearly melted with desire.

"I am locking the front door," he said with a smile.

"I'll be waiting," said Helen, walking unsteadily toward the bedroom. Her gown floated after her.

When Frank returned, Helen was lying facedown on the bed. A bottle of Dom Perignon was beside her on the pillow. She was passed out.

Frank stared out the window. He was stone cold sober. He had a wife. He was no longer alone. In a few weeks, they would start 1924 with a new life in Hollywood. A mournful horn sounded. The fog was rolling in. Frank closed the window and lay back on the bed, fully clothed. He stared at the ceiling. Helen snored softly next to him. His wedding night had not turned out exactly as he had planned. But that was just like life. The only place where life turned out like you dreamed was the movies.

Chapter Four

THE EMBRACE OF LAUGHTER

Helen threw her head back and laughed uproariously at something Tony said. She had never looked more beautiful. Frank's brothers Tony and Ben, who had come with Ben's family to Los Angeles from Sacramento to welcome Helen and celebrate the marriage, were obviously enchanted with her.

Sarrida had laid out a spread in the front yard of the house on Albion Street. The whole neighborhood had turned out. It was a Sunday evening in late January 1924 and unseasonably warm. People drifted in and out drinking Sarrida's homemade wine. Frank noticed the more sinister aspects of the neighborhood that hadn't changed. Some of the neighbors, unknown to him, looked like bootleggers. "A shady character looks the same the world over," he thought to himself.

Frank was tired. He was more than ready to return to their two-room apartment on Gower. Tomorrow he would start his first day at Hal Roach's studio in Culver City. Rob Wagner had introduced him to Robert McGowan, one of Roach's directors, and McGowan had agreed to give him a trial as a writer for the

Our Gang comedies. Frank wanted to make a good impression in this, his first studio job.

The family loved Helen. They begged Frank to play his ukulele. He didn't want to. He quietly told Helen he wanted to leave. "He's a little stick in the mud, that's what he is," said Helen with a whinny. "One little dance honey." Helen arose unsteadily from the chair where she had been sitting between Tony and Ben. She raised her glass of wine over her head and hummed a tune while she shimmied her hips. Frank's brothers and several other males from the neighborhood clapped approvingly.

Tony slid over to Frank and asked, "If she's this wild and fun here, what happens when you get home, Frankie?" He wiggled his eyebrows suggestively and chuckled loudly.

Frank wanted to punch him. Instead, he pried the wineglass out of Helen's grip, took her arm, and said resolutely, "We are going. Now."

"Ohhh, spoilsport! Just when I'm having fun," warbled Helen. Frank pulled her down the sidewalk toward their car. Sarrida ran after them with party food wrapped in napkins. She shoved it inside the window where Helen was collapsed against the car seat. Then she turned to face Frank.

"This is a good girl, Frankie. Nice. I can tell. But Frankie, she needs to eat more and drink less."

Frank drove home and got his wife inside their stuffy apartment. He laid her carefully on their bed. She was very drunk and mumbling something. "The sweetest little Italian immigrants . . . poor but sweet . . . so sweet."

Bile rose inside him and his stomach churned. Helen had been observing his family as though they were specimens in a zoo. To her, they would never be more than poor immigrants. She had been slumming that evening, getting a taste of immigrants and their lives.

Frank arrived at the gates of Roach's studio at 8:00 a.m. the next day. Bob McGowan was there to meet him. He was a tall, rangy man with a deeply tanned face and calloused hands. He walked with a limp.

"It's from an accident that happened when I was a fireman in Colorado. That's what I did before coming to this nuthouse," McGowan explained as they walked slowly past offices, painted flats leaning against walls, rolling iron carts full of equipment, and sleepy crew members smoking and drinking coffee out of paper cups.

"I work for Mr. Roach, who owns this place," McGowan went on. "And you report to me, see. You can write out the scenarios on pieces of paper that you can give me at the end of each day. If they're good, we'll use 'em and you'll get paid at the end of the week. If they're bad, you'll get fired. Got it? And you don't need an office, right? It's California, so it's always good weather. Enjoy it and find a table on the lot."

McGowan thrust a pad and several pencils at Frank, saying, "I'll expect this pad to be filled by the end of the day." He began to limp away, then said over his shoulder, "I'm kidding you. But not entirely. Mr. Roach expects results."

Frank found a woodpile in the shade and began working.

As the sun rose, even on a January day, it grew hot. A shadow appeared over his writing pad a little after noon. Frank looked up to see Will Rogers leaning over him. By this time in Rogers's career, the humorist, actor, and former vaudeville performer from Oklahoma was one of the most famous men in America. His slate blue eyes peered intently into Frank's dark ones.

"You've got real concentration, kid," Rogers said. "I have been standing here for some time. You're working as if your life depends on it. Who are you writing for?"

"I'm not allowed to say exactly, but yes, my life does sort of depend on it, or at least my paycheck. I'm Frank Capra, and I'm a big fan of your work." Frank put out his hand and Rogers shook it with a firm grip.

"Must be McGowan and Roach," said Rogers. "I'm working for them, too. But they aren't trying to fry me to death. You are going to get heatstroke sitting out here, and then you won't be any good to anybody. Tell you what. They made a fancy place for me to stay while I'm working, and it's bigger than many homes I've lived in. Why don't you sit in there? There's free donuts and coffee and a place to lie down, which is what I do when I tell folks I'm working. You are welcome to it, Frank Capra."

For six months, Frank labored at the Roach studios writing for the *Our Gang* series and handing his work to McGowan. Some of his scripts, but not all, were accepted. "Big Town," a classic *Our Gang* caper, was written by Frank. Set in New York City, it referenced iconic landmarks including the Statue of Liberty, the Flatiron Building and the Brooklyn Bridge. The story line was about a wealthy aunt who insists on adopting

Mickey, one of the gang. Classic sight gags, such as a kitchen skating rink made of soap bubbles and the whack of a board to a policeman's bottom, hinted at what was to become a favorite Frank Capra theme: skewering upper-class pretensions.

Frank based some of his story ideas on real people and events from his childhood. For example, he wrote about a fight promoter at Alameda and Main in downtown Los Angeles who would set up free-for-alls among the tougher newsboys. He would offer new pairs of shoes to those who could fight for them in a pile. Onlookers would take bets on the fisticuffs. McGowan deemed scenarios like this one to be "too real," and Frank began to tire of what he considered the sentimental comedies. He wanted to work on material that was more daring.

Rob Wagner, who seemed to know everyone in Hollywood, suggested that Frank ask for an interview with Mack Sennett, whose *Keystone Cops* were, if anything, more anarchic and adult than the *Our Gang* series. Meanwhile, Helen was growing bored with her life in Hollywood. When Frank returned from the Roach Studios at night, he often found their small apartment crowded with denizens Helen had picked up from bars on Hollywood Boulevard. Once he had cleared them out, arguments ensued.

"There is nothing to eat, and this place is a mess," Frank would say.

"I'm not your maid. Hire one or you can make your own food," Helen snapped.

"Why don't you look for work or go to casting offices?" Frank asked.

"I've got better things to do than to sit around all day with a bunch of floozies waiting to be picked."

"What other things, honey?" Frank wanted to know. "Occupying real estate on a stool at the Pig 'n Whistle? You've become a fixture there."

The arguments would continue until one of them slammed out of the house to seek solace elsewhere.

It was difficult for Frank to concentrate on his marriage. He was driven by thoughts of what he wanted to accomplish. It was clear to him now, after watching Bob McGowan direct the cast and crew for the *Our Gang* comedies. He admired the kindness and ease McGowan displayed toward the actors. He watched them visibly relax under McGowan's tutelage. No matter what madness was going on elsewhere, McGowan always remained calm with his actors. Frank wanted to be a director. He wanted to tell stories that would make people feel, not just laugh. He would bide his time. The chance would come.

In late September 1925, just as the heat of the day was beginning to recede, Frank was walking despondently to the streetcar in Culver City. It had been a long day at the Roach Studio. Another script had been rejected by McGowan as being "too real." Frank was contemplating what exactly this meant when he ran into Rob Wagner, who was there for a script conference.

"You are a sight for sore eyes, Frank," said Wagner. "Where have you been keeping yourself?"

"In the Hal Roach playpen," said Frank.

"You need to step out, Frank. I'm going to get you an introduction to Mack Sennett. I said I would, and I will."

Wagner was as good as his word. Two weeks later, Frank found himself giving his name to the guard at Keystone Studios in Edendale, a pleasant suburban enclave between downtown and the San Fernando Valley.

"What are you here for, fella?" asked the guard.

"I've come to Edendale to interview for a job to write for Mack Sennett," answered Frank.

"You'll find it's no Eden," the guard replied. "But let me give you some advice. See those lovely gals?" He opened the gate and positioned Frank where he could see a group of young women, some wearing bathing suits and others draped in robes. They were all beautiful. "Look, but don't touch," said the guard. "Don't ever touch. Don't ask one out for a drink or a movie. Nothing. Get me?"

Frank nodded slowly.

Next, the guard pointed out a huge, hulking woman with a thatch of red hair. She resembled a female Viking. "Now see that gal? She protects the Old Man's bathing beauties."

Frank nodded again.

The guard was satisfied. "Okay, go down three streets, take a left, and go back in the corner, see. Then you'll get to the Tower. You can see it from here. That's where Old Man Sennett keeps his gaggle of writers."

Frank shaded his eyes and spotted a rickety looking three-story structure that leaned slightly, as if peeking over the entire lot. "The Old Man—that's Sennett, see—he's got a marble bathtub up there in his office and a window overlooking the lot so's he can see if anyone's cheating him. Good luck, young man."

Frank was well aware of the storied nature of the Keystone Studios and its comedy legacy. Starting as a singer and low-rung vaudevillian, Sennett had landed in Hollywood in 1912. He bought property that year in Edendale, a residential area between Burbank and Hollywood. He had a knack for spotting and nurturing talent, and his company of first-rate comedians and actors soon included Fatty Arbuckle, Ben Turpin, Chester Conklin, eventually Charlie Chaplin, and, at the center of it all, Mabel Normand, a brilliant actress and comedienne with whom Sennett was in love. They carried on a tempestuous romance for over a decade. By the time Frank made his way into employment as a writer for Sennett, the romance had soured. Sennett carried a flame for Normand his entire life.

Sennett spent long days, every day, overseeing the creation of comedic moments and crafting them into silent film comedy masterpieces that thrilled and entertained audiences through the mid-1920s. Doing so required continually building new comedy sequences and ever more daring acts of physical challenge to keep audiences coming back. Central to the work of Keystone Studios was the physicality of the actors. All were athletic and supremely skilled at making their precisely timed pratfalls look easy and improvised. One of their most famous gags was pie throwing, which they honed to a science.

Keystone Studios needed stories, however simple, on which to hang their comedic genius, and Sennett hired whole groups of writers to work in the room above his office. He hired Frank Capra on the spot when he saw that Frank was not fazed by the fact that Sennett conducted his job interview while taking a bubble bath in his marble tub.

Sennett had a habit of attempting to sneak up on the writers' room to see if anyone was loafing. The stairs always creaked, warning the writers of Sennett's approach. So he hired carpenters to fix the stairs. Frank Capra, the engineer, got to the carpenters first and had them make one step that was higher than the rest, causing Sennett to trip on it each time, swearing, cursing, and thus alerting the writers.

Frank observed the directors on the lot with an eye toward his own desired future. When he read his scenarios aloud, he often acted them out, even perfecting the art of standing on his head. He worked with extreme focus, and though friendly with his colleagues, he made it clear that he was there to succeed. He was going to be more than a writer of gags.

Frank's chance to direct came in the form of a doughy-faced vaudeville performer named Harry Langdon. Sennett often scouted and put on contract performers and comedians he thought had star potential. He had been right about Mabel Normand and many others who started out working with him. Langdon was attractive to Sennett because of his successful vaudeville career. Langdon's wife, Rose, was part of his act. Born in Council Bluffs, Iowa, Langdon had been working in vaude-ville for almost twenty years by the time he was hired by Sennett.

Once Sennett brought Langdon to Keystone Studios, he had no idea what to do with him. Unlike the frenetic Keystone Cops and other comedians who populated Sennett's films with lightning-paced antics, Langdon was slow, simple, and deliberate. The writers were baffled as to how to write for him. The directors were also stumped.

Frank realized immediately that Langdon's audience appeal was that of the innocent, naive man who makes his way through the evils of the world and eventually triumphs. He was certain that developing scenarios like that for Langdon would make him a hit with filmgoers. Frank convinced Sennett to allow him and Arthur Ripley, another writer, to work solely with Langdon. Frank assisted in shaping, for all of Langdon's characters, the "principle of the brick." Langdon could be saved by a brick falling on an enemy, but he could never cause the brick's fall.

While Frank was developing material for Langdon, he saved enough money to buy a property at 6480 Odin Street. He built a Spanish home in the hills overlooking the newly built Hollywood Bowl. It had four bedrooms, one of which was fitted out as a nursery. Helen had recently found out she was pregnant. They hung wallpaper imprinted with storks on a rare Sunday when Frank was not working. Frank and Helen were delighted with this turn of events, although Helen still complained that she was lonely. Frank invited Sarrida, his sister, Anne, and an actor friend, Al Roscoe, to live in the house and fill it with people, thinking they could fill in for him.

In the meantime, Harry Langdon became a huge star. He divorced his wife, took to driving a huge limousine, and decided to leave Mack Sennett and Keystone after other studios made him lucrative offers. First National Pictures promised him his own production company, and he leapt at the chance. He offered Frank Capra the opportunity to direct for him, and Frank agreed. He would finally be able to realize his dream.

It was 1926, and Frank was getting what he wanted since the time he had looked through the camera at Montague's studio. He was going to direct *The Strong Man*, Langdon's second feature. On the day he signed with Langdon, Frank made his way home to celebrate with Helen. He bought roses from a florist on Franklin and wound his way up Odin Street. When he opened the door, he saw his wife slumped on the horsehair sofa. He dropped the roses.

"You've been drinking," he said accusingly. "In the middle of the day."

"I lost the baby, Frank!" Helen wailed. "And they say I'll never be able to have another. So I am going to drink as much as I want, whenever I want, and you can't stop me." Brandishing a half-empty bottle of gin, she staggered up the stairs, clutching the wrought iron railing.

Frank stood silently in shock. Before long, he heard a ripping sound. He climbed slowly up the stairs to the nursery. Helen was using her fingernails to shred the stork wallpaper. It hung like palm fronds over the soft white carpet. Frank tried to embrace Helen to comfort her, but she flinched and screamed at him to leave the room.

Frank made his way down the stairs. Sarrida stood in the doorway to the kitchen. "We all lose things. Tragedies happen," she said, "but it's no excuse to drink like that."

Frank turned on his heel and walked out the front door. He stood on the front porch of the house he had purchased with a salary he'd made working in the movies. He got into his car and returned to First National and the Langdon studio. The guard waved him through the gate and he felt a sense of calm. This was now his home.

In *The Strong Man*, Frank was able to make full use of Langdon's appeal. As an innocent soldier kidnapped by a circus strongman, his character searches for and ultimately finds the sweet young blind woman who has written him letters at the front. Along the way, he confronts big city evil in the form of an unscrupulous gangster's moll as well as small town corruption. The two main female figures in the film are the rapacious, menacing moll, Lily of Broadway (Gertrude Astor) and the innocent pastor's daughter, Mary Brown (Priscilla Bonner).

Langdon was pitch-perfect in his scenes on film. Off camera, he was laconic and unfriendly. Frank enjoyed working with the actors and began to understand that each one had their own unique creative psychology. He developed ways of working with them individually to make them understand what he wanted. Some preferred long conferences and others just needed to be left alone.

The Strong Man was a hit with audiences. Frank was certain that he had found the secret to success with Langdon. They began to make plans for the next Langdon feature, *Tramp, Tramp, Tramp*.

Things began to fall apart for Langdon and his company during the filming of *Tramp, Tramp, Tramp*. Langdon had no idea how to run a production company and began to listen to sycophants. He made arbitrary and senseless business decisions. Frank may have empathized, initially, with Langdon's character's innocence. The theme of the duplicitous nature of women resonated in *The Strong Man, Tramp, Tramp, Tramp,* and *Long Pants,* a third film begun at Langdon's company. But as Langdon grew more imperious and began to crumble under the pressures of running his own company, his relationship with Frank began to fray.

Frank decided to confront Langdon directly about his peevishness and destructive behavior. He left no stone unturned, detailing the negative effect of Langdon's behavior on the cast, crew, and ultimately the company he was supposedly running. Langdon listened to Frank's tirade while lying on a cot in his trailer. His wide eyes and passive expression showed no emotion. He said nothing in response. Frank realized he was not going to get an answer and stormed out.

It was late fall 1927. Frank drove home from the studio in the twilight. The sun was an orange ball setting over the Hollywood Bowl. As he made his way up the driveway, he could hear Sarrida's voice through an open window. It didn't sound happy. He turned around and made his way to the dress shop on Hollywood Boulevard that he had bought for Helen and his sister Anne. They had developed the idea of creating designs for women in Hollywood, and Frank had jumped at the chance to give his wife something to do.

The front of the shop was empty. Frank heard voices coming from the back room. A radio was playing. He pushed aside the flowered curtain and saw his wife dancing with a man he didn't know. A bottle of expensive Scotch sat on the table. "Frank, this is Adolfo from my acting class," Helen said. "We're rehearsing a scene." The two of them started to giggle.

"Get out," said Frank quietly. "Let go of my wife and get out."

When Adolfo was gone, Helen sat unsteadily at the table.

"We were just rehearsing," she said, leaning her head on her hand.

"Where is Anne?" asked Frank.

"Your mamma came to get her. I guess she doesn't like her hanging around with a real woman."

Frank was furious. He swallowed hard and said, "Let's go home."

"She called me a whore, you know. She liked me so much at first butter wouldn't melt. She was glad you didn't marry some Italian immigrant girl. But when she saw I wouldn't kowtow. . . ," Helen drifted off, laughing to herself and shrugging her shoulders.

When they reached home, Sarrida ran outside. "Someone is trying to reach you from the Langdon company," she said, with a worried look on her face. "They've called three times."

As Frank walked up the stairs with Helen, who was barely able to stand, he heard the phone ringing.

"It's them again," said Sarrida, "I'll take her."

Sarrida put a practiced arm around her daughter-in-law and helped her to her bedroom.

Frank picked up the phone and said "Yes?" with a feeling of dread.

"Frank, it's Murray, Harry's assistant."

"I know who you are, Murray," said Frank.

"Frank, there is no easy way to say this. You're fired. Harry doesn't want to see you again at the studio, or anywhere ever again. We'll send over your last paycheck and a box of your stuff tomorrow. And Frank . . . don't say I told you, but he's going to try to take away your directing credit for *Long Pants*. You didn't hear that from me, though. You are a good guy, Frank. Talented. You deserve better. Langdon's become impossible. I like you. Good luck to you, Frank Capra."

Murray hung up. Frank heard a rushing sound in his ears. His stomach churned. He sat down at the phone table, grabbed a piece of paper, and wrote a letter detailing his work on *Long Pants* and the difficulties involved. Then he sent it to the trade papers.

Because of Langdon's prominence in the industry, Hollywood buzzed about Frank's letter for weeks. Some people chose to believe Langdon's claim that Frank Capra had little to do with *Long Pants*. Others chose to believe Frank Capra. The resulting rumors affected Frank negatively. His phone stopped ringing. Then he got a call from First National, offering him a picture to direct in New York City. It was titled *For the Love of Mike*, and the cast and crew were already in place.

Frank wanted to get away from California, his wife, his mother, and his house on Odin Street. He took the job, went to New York, and faced a poorly produced film that had such precarious financing the actors insisted on being paid each day before they began shooting. In the end, there was no money left to pay the director, and Frank ended up hitchhiking back to Los Angeles.

The film was not a success. The lead actress was a young and beautiful Broadway star named Claudette Colbert. She hated doing the film and declared she would never work in the movies again.

Frank returned to Hollywood shortly before the premiere of *Long Pants*. He was determined to attend the event, to dispel any notion that he had not actually directed it. Anne tailored a new tuxedo for him and designed a gown for Helen to wear. Frank begged Helen to be sober for the occasion, and she gave him her word.

He was nervous about the evening and arrived home after a long meeting with a potential agent. Agents were just beginning to become businesses in their own right, and Frank felt he needed representation. The meeting had not gone well, as he had been questioned about Harry Langdon.

Helen was dressed. She was leaning against the stone archway that led to the living room. It seemed to be holding her up. Her lipstick was smeared. Mascara was running down her cheeks. She lurched forward and said, "I couldn't do it. I couldn't do it sober. Not for you. Not for anybody."

Frank didn't think. He just reacted. He slapped her. She stared at him uncomprehendingly. Frank felt a rush of shame and regret. Helen crumpled to the floor, holding her cheek. Frank bent over her saying, "I am so sorry, baby. So sorry! Forgive me. Please forgive me." She waved him away. Frank stood up and saw

Sarrida in the doorway to the kitchen. Her arms were crossed and she shook her head with disapproval.

Frank moved out that night and found a room at the Hollywood Athletic Club. Helen filed for divorce soon after. Frank received the notice in his mailbox at the Athletic Club on a hot September day in 1927. He was thirty years old. He read it and decided to take a walk down Sunset Boulevard, even though it was during the heat of the day. As he walked down Wilcox toward Hollywood Boulevard, he saw a familiar tall figure loping along ahead of him. It was his old boss, Mack Sennett.

Sennett was more than empathetic about Frank's divorce and full of advice about women and life. He insisted Frank join him for liver and onions at the Musso and Frank Grill on Hollywood Boulevard. They sat in a red leather booth for hours, late into the afternoon. Sennett seemed reluctant to let Frank go. He'd had more than a few martinis. He kept going over and over his regrets about Mabel Normand.

"I just didn't love her enough, Frankie," Sennett said. "Don't ever get involved with actresses. They'll break your heart every time. I tell you what. Come back and work for me, Frank. You're an intellectual, a college guy. We need some smarts over there to give us some class."

Frank agreed to come back, then called a cab and helped Sennett into it. He gave the driver Sennett's address and thought of the palatial mansion in Westmoreland Place Sennett owned. Frank had visited there. It was full of empty rooms, dining tables at which no one sat and a swimming pool no one used. "Sennett knows how to run a studio, but not his own life," thought Frank.

Frank went back to Sennett for a few weeks, but his heart wasn't in it. One evening in early October, he was summoned to the front desk of the Hollywood Athletic Club. Abe, who ran the desk, told him he had an important phone call. Abe knew the backstory of every person who entered or exited the club. He made it his business to do so. He was a one-man gossip column.

"It's Harry Cohn's office, Mr. Capra," Abe said. He put his hand over the receiver. "You know who Harry Cohn is, right, Mr. Capra? They call him the prince of Poverty Row."

Frank took the receiver and held it to his ear. Before he could say anything, a loud voice rumbled, "Capra, Sam Briskin here. I'm the head of production at Columbia Pictures and my boss, Harry Cohn, wants to see you tomorrow at 2:00 p.m. sharp. Got it?"

Frank said, "Yes, I—" and before he could say anything else, Briskin replied "Good!" and hung up.

Of course, Abe had heard every word. Frank looked at Abe and whistled through his teeth. He raised his eyebrows as if to say, "Should I do it?"

Abe understood completely. "Take the meeting. But show him who's boss, see?" Frank thought that was some of the best advice he'd had in a long time.

Chapter Five

THE EMBRACE OF STORYTELLING

Frank walked with purpose down Gower Street in Hollywood. It was one of those early fall days in California that didn't feel like fall. The heat was already shimmering up from the sidewalk, but Frank had decided to go on foot to his interview with Harry Cohn. He kept up a brisk pace despite the heat and strolled past the side entrance to the Paramount studios.

He considered the work going on beyond those walls. The Big Five studios, Paramount, MGM, Twentieth Century-Fox, RKO, and Warner Bros., were all established entities with major stars. The studios were run on the model of Henry Ford. Recognizable pieces of equipment, in this case movie stars, were put together with stories with factory-like precision to create products that would attract audiences to buy tickets. Most of the studios had invested in building movie palaces. They spent money on star salaries, scenario writers, publicity departments, lavish costumes, and sets. Their studios covered vast acres of land in Culver City, Universal City, and the San Fernando Valley. The studio heads basked in their power and represented themselves as the royalty of Hollywood.

Harry Cohn and Columbia Pictures, where Frank was headed, had none of those things. As he crossed Melrose and continued north on Gower, Frank realized that the advantage in taking a directing job at Columbia might be the very fact that it was smaller and not set up as a vast machine. He thought over the experience he'd had thus far, with Hal Roach and Mack Sennett. He realized that freedom might lie in the ability to have control over the final product. He would ask for this kind of control, even though he had no illusions about the man with whom he was interviewing.

Harry Cohn had a reputation. Born In New York City in 1881, he came from a Jewish immigrant background. His father was a tailor who specialized in policemen's uniforms. His mother, Bella, specialized in making sure the customers paid their bills. She was relentless in collecting payments, but also often surrounded by policemen. Perhaps this early respect for the law influenced Harry Cohn. He drove a hard bargain, but once the agreement was made, he always came through.

Cohn originally wanted to be a professional singer but grew discouraged with performing. Recognizing early on the public's interest in movies, he and his brother Jack started a company that made shorts to go with popular songs. In 1920, when they expanded to two-reelers, they decided they needed someone to promote business in California. At first, Cohn went to work for Carl Laemmle, the founder and owner of Universal Pictures.

However, he soon branched out on his own with his brother Jack and Joe Brandt, a lawyer and accountant who was brought in as a partner. They sought financing from the banker A. P. Giannini, the founder of what would become the Bank of America, and by 1922 had begun making short films.

Jack Cohn and Joe Brandt stayed in New York City and Harry Cohn became the vice president of production in Hollywood. The company was initially called CBC. When wags started referring to it as Corned Beef and Cabbage, it was renamed Columbia Pictures. At Columbia, there was constant tension between the East Coast and the West Coast. Jack held the purse strings. Harry chose the material and the casts and oversaw production. The two brothers fought viciously and constantly, each accusing the other of profligacy and incompetence via coast-to-coast phone calls. Joe Brandt was stuck in the middle.

When Frank Capra came to interview at Columbia in October 1927, this way of working was long established. Harry and Jack Cohn were belligerent and aggressive toward each another and their employees. But the tension seemed to create a system of checks and balances that resulted in a profitable business.

Columbia had purchased a set of ramshackle buildings at Sunset and Gower going east toward Beechwood Drive. They had made the crucial decision not to build or purchase movie theaters. Instead, they relied on box office draw to convince theater owners to put Columbia Pictures on the bill. This allowed Columbia to focus on creating product, not maintaining theaters. As Harry Cohn liked to say, "Give the public what they want and they will come out for it."

Jack Cohn's strict budgets also dictated the kinds of films Columbia made. They were mainly films that could be shot on tiny stages. There were no period films; too expensive. No musicals; too complicated. No films with complicated locations; too unpredictable. Crowd scenes and the use of extras were kept to a minimum. Extras were often plucked from the streets moments before shooting. Stock footage from other sources was used. Sets were reused, repainted, borrowed from the bigger studios, or bought when other studios were through using them. Actors often wore their own costumes and did their own makeup.

To avoid the costly $400 location fee the city of Los Angeles charged for shooting on the street, cameras were set up, shots were hurried, and equipment and actors were rushed away before they could be found out. Nothing stopped the workday at Columbia. It was sacrosanct. If it rained while shooting outdoors and it was supposed to be sunny, the script was changed to accommodate the weather.

Harry Cohn himself was a dapper, meticulously dressed, imposing man with a large head and startling ice blue eyes. He relished wielding his power and regarded every meeting as a competition. He made snap judgments, working on hunches, and ruled over Columbia Pictures with an iron hand.

Cohn arrived at noon each day and often stayed at the studio until midnight, going over the rushes from the previous day. If the work didn't please him, threats and firings followed. When he wasn't on the phone barking orders or arguing with his brother Jack, he was staring out the window overlooking the front gate to see who was coming and going. Anyone who was late was given a personal warning. If it happened again, they were fired.

Cohn was perpetually on the lookout for waste of any kind. It was not tolerated. He walked the lot every day, turning an eagle eye on every department. If a light bulb was left burning in an empty room, if a sheet of paper was wasted, if an employee was caught taking what he considered an unearned break, there was hell to pay.

Once, when he spotted an actress taking up valuable time in the makeup chair, he insisted they make up only half her face and shoot the scene from the side. Flats were used over and over. Cohn was known to sneak up on workers in every department, from lighting to janitorial. He knew every single employee, and he demanded the utmost loyalty and 100 percent effort from everyone.

When Frank met Harry Cohn, he was married to Rose Cohn, a woman he had met several years before on a trip to New York. She was already married, but Cohn fell in love with her. He spirited her to Hollywood and wooed her away from her marriage with a display of stars, wealth, and luxury. The couple was childless, although Rose raised their two orphaned nieces as their own.

Cohn had a battered old piano in his office, a remnant of his days as a singer, and he often had composers use it for tryouts, passing immediate judgment on their talents. A discreet door in his office led to dressing rooms used by actresses. Cohn was not above making frequent use of it for liaisons. Another door led to a marble washroom with a shower for Cohn's personal use, as he was fanatically clean. His language was crude in the extreme and he did not hesitate to use it to make his opinions known.

Cohn had a specific way of testing any artist, male or female, seeking work at Columbia. He almost always insulted their previous work or talent and then sat back to see how they would respond. If they were stunned, deeply hurt, or burst into tears, they were shown the door. If they tried to defend their work, they were told to clear out. But if they shouted back at Cohn and told him, in so many words, to go to hell, Cohn would hire them on the spot, declaring that he was just testing them to see if they believed in themselves.

There was another side to Harry Cohn. If you proved that you could assist Columbia in creating product that was successful, meaning films that made a profit, you would continue to receive a paycheck. The close proximity of all the departments at Columbia, and the fact that once you proved your worth to him, Cohn would respect you by allowing you a certain freedom, gave a kind of unity to the work at Columbia. Cohn had an astounding knack for picking out talent in all departments, and as Columbia grew in stature, it attracted some of the most respected talent in all of Hollywood. Employees enjoyed a kind of camaraderie that was impossible at other behemoth studios.

Cohn had a philosophy of casting actors who were either stars on the descent at other studios or in some kind of feud, whether legal or artistic, with other, larger studios. He took special glee in spiriting stars away from other studios, especially when he knew that large sums of money had been spent to promote their careers.

One thing Cohn desired more than anything was respect from the Hollywood community, mainly his arch competitors: MGM's Louis B. Mayer, Adolph Zukor of Paramount Pictures, and the Warner brothers, Harry, Albert, Sam, and Jack. Another thing he wanted more than anything was an Academy Award, the ultimate symbol of recognition. His notion of talent was summed up by something he repeated often: "If you have talent, I will kiss your ass. If you don't, I'll kick it."

Frank was aware of Cohn's reputation and the lowly position Columbia occupied in the hierarchy of Hollywood in October 1927. Columbia Pictures was located at 1438 Gower. As Frank made his way there, he passed hordes of people standing under the awnings of the businesses at Sunset and Gower. Many were actual cowboys who until recently had been wrangling horses on ranches in the San Fernando Valley. They had heard there was easy money to be made working in the movies. Others were young women and men who had come to Hollywood from all over the country seeking employment as extras. They hoped to be the next Mary Pickford or Douglas Fairbanks. They loitered near the drugstores and coffee shops on Sunset Boulevard, waiting for a call for extras from Central Casting or the many Poverty Row studios that surrounded the area.

Frank walked through the gate and assessed Columbia Pictures. The buildings were small, colorless, and unimpressive. There was no rhyme or reason to the design or placement. He made his way up stairs so narrow it would be impossible for anyone to pass. The only sound he heard was a cacophony of voices shouting.

He reached Sam Briskin's office. Briskin was the head of production. Frank supposed he had been sent there as a prelude to meeting Cohn himself. Frank was ready.

He was ushered into a tiny cubicle. Briskin sat behind a desk that looked more like a spindly nightstand. He wore thick glasses. He didn't get up when Frank put out his hand. He regarded Frank with a long stare and said, finally, "You are awfully short, even for a dago."

Frank said nothing. He looked back at Briskin with a steady gaze.

Briskin cocked his head to one side and said, "If you come to work at Columbia, you'll have to make a better picture than *For the Love of Mike*. What a stinker, eh?"

In a slow, even tone, Frank replied, "You can go to hell. I didn't come here for this." He turned and walked out into the stifling hallway. He slammed the door so hard the thin walls shook. Something fell off the wall and crashed to the floor. Frank was halfway down the stairs when Briskin caught up with him.

"Hey, hey, hey fella, I didn't mean it," Briskin said. "I'm kidding you. Don't take it so hard. Harry Cohn is waiting to meet you. He wants to make you an offer to direct. He's upstairs."

Frank turned and took in Briskin. He considered his options. He had come this far. He figured he might as well see Cohn. Besides, he was curious to meet the man who already had a reputation in Hollywood as a brash, hard-bitten competitor. He felt he had nothing to lose.

Briskin gestured for Frank to follow him up the stairs to the third floor. A pleasant secretary who introduced herself as Dorothy said, "Mr. Cohn is waiting for you."

There was no outside handle to Cohn's office door. Any visitor had to be buzzed in. When the door opened, Frank found himself looking at a man at a desk on a raised platform at the end of a long room. A battered piano sat on the right wall. The man was yelling into a phone. The desk held several other phones, one of which was ringing. The man didn't seem to be waiting for anyone. He seemed to be in the midst of a negotiation that was not going his way. He paused during a stream of invective, looked Frank over and turned his head toward Briskin, who silently nodded.

"Okay," said Cohn loudly, barely skipping a beat in his phone conversation, "hire him for one picture. If he's good, he can stay. Otherwise, he's out. Now scram."

Briskin and Frank stood awkwardly for a moment, and Cohn waved at them with a beefy hand. "I said get out!"

Back in Briskin's office, Briskin offered Frank $1,000 to direct *That Certain Thing*, a romantic comedy already on the Columbia slate, to be budgeted at $20,000. He was surprised when Frank accepted the offer with no negotiation. He was equally surprised when Frank said, "But I want full control over directing, casting, writing, and editing. If I can't have that, I'm out."

Briskin studied him carefully and said, "You can have it. But it better be good, or it will all fall on you. And it will be your first and last picture for Harry Cohn."

Frank was at the studio the next day by 7:00 a.m. He had already made out a location list, shot lists, and a cast list. All of the actors were already known to audiences, including Viola Dana, a durable silent film veteran. The storyline involved a young couple, one a millionaire rejected by his family, starting a successful rival box lunch business that eventually garners the attention and approval of his father. Ralph Graves, another veteran actor Frank had come to know at Mack Sennett's, was to play the young man. Frank arrived at his assigned office, a tiny cubicle not much bigger than his bathroom at the Hollywood Athletic Club, just as the sun was coming up.

Frank's first visitor was Joseph Walker, a noted cinematographer who had been assigned by Harry Cohn to work on *That Certain Thing*. Walker was already a highly respected professional. He had been fascinated by cameras as a young boy growing up in Venice, California. His first opportunity to see a film company at work was when he came upon Mack Sennett acting in a film on location in one of the canals right outside Walker's boyhood home. Billy Bitzer, who would become one of the most famous cameramen in the silent era, was behind the camera that day. He spoke kindly with Walker, explaining how the camera worked, and from then on, Walker was hooked.

Walker was an engineering genius and spent time during his teenage years pioneering wireless communication. His innovations had already attracted the attention of the Wright Brothers and Lee de Forest, another innovator in the field.

Walker began working with D. W. Griffith and Billy Bitzer in 1914. Those were the days before guards at movie studios. He just walked through the Griffith Studio gates at 4500 Sunset Boulevard and introduced himself to Bitzer a second time. Starting as an assistant to Bitzer, Walker took careful note of everything Bitzer and Griffith did, as their work was so obviously superior to any other filmmakers of the time.

Walker shot his first feature film, *Back to God's Country*, with the intrepid actress Nell Shipman in the Arctic in 1919. He began experimenting with diffusion lenses. They could be switched out to change focus so shooting could continue without interruption or stopping the action to change camera position. Walker initially developed diffusion lenses as a time saver while working on Westerns on Poverty Row.

When Walker came to Columbia in 1927, he was thirty-five years old and a veteran of twenty-seven films. Harry Cohn had given him the usual gruff and combative hiring interview. Cohn was especially interested in Walker's ability, known even then, to make leading ladies look glamorous. Walker had pioneered the use of key lights, tiny lights that were strong and focused and set near the camera lens. They made blemished skin glow with alabaster highlights, artfully sculpted cheekbones, and created liquid, luminous eyes. Aware of Cohn's reputation, Walker had stood up to him in a way that impressed Cohn, who hired Walker on the spot to photograph the female star of his next film, Dorothy Revier.

In his first film for Columbia, Walker made the actors look enticing and the cheap sets look luxurious. Cohn immediately realized Walker's talent and his value to the company. He assigned Walker to work with fledgling Frank Capra as a hedge against Capra's relative inexperience.

When Walker saw Frank sitting behind a miniscule desk in a tiny office on the Columbia lot, he mistook him for a young boy. He couldn't believe this was the director to whom he had been assigned. Walker remembered that Frank was connected to Mack Sennett and Harry Langdon. He did not relish working with someone who had only directed comedies. Having made nearly thirty films, Walker resisted the notion of being assigned to a rookie director.

He was soon convinced otherwise. Frank's focus and intensity, in addition to his obvious passion for filmmaking, were unmistakable.

Frank didn't waste a minute. "We need to get right down to business here," he said, looking straight at Walker. "I respect your work and I understand you don't know me at all. Fair enough. But I know that what we need here, for this picture, is clarity and economy. Nothing fancy. Nothing arty."

"Do you realize what it takes to make these cheap sets and flimsy props look like something?" Walker shot back. "Do you have any idea what I have to do to make an actress Cohn has hired on the cheap because she's a known quantity but on the skids from MGM and ten years too old for the part look like a dewy ingénue?"

Frank broke into a wide grin. He spent the next hour asking Walker about his lenses, and how exactly he created the diffusion and lighting that made magic out of nothing. He was eager to learn and interested in every aspect of Walker's work. At the end of the hour, the two men had become friends and colleagues.

"I hear everything you are saying," Frank said. "I understand. Believe me, we are on the same page. We are on the same team here."

Walker was flattered by Frank's curiosity and struck by his ability to understand both the science and the art behind his work. A working partnership was formed that would last through the following decade and create unforgettable moments in twenty films.

One of the plans Frank devised was to economize by grouping close-ups, medium shots, and long shots, when possible, to save the time it took to relight and reset for every shot. The result was a first day's rush of all close-ups. When Cohn, who had been on vacation when Frank began shooting, settled in to see the new director's rushes, he became apoplectic and screamed for Briskin to fire Capra immediately. When Cohn realized Frank's ingenious way to save time and money, he was duly impressed.

Frank brought in the film on time, in less than six weeks. It received positive reviews and made a tidy profit for Columbia. Audiences who flocked to *That Certain Thing* were charmed not only by the storyline, which pitted youth and ingenuity against upper-class intransigence, but by the humor and moments of authentic human behavior.

The film opens with Viola Dana, the heroine, giving her little brothers a bubble bath. The boys throw bubbles and splash water, and a bubble fight ensues. The water drips down to the apartment below, where a portly woman berates her dog about the puddle on the floor. Meanwhile, Dana's mother, who is in the tenement kitchen washing dishes, snatches crumbs and bits of leftovers from the plates she is cleaning. These beautifully observed small details and moments of behavior combine in a succinct and truthful portrait of real life in the tenement apartment and draw the viewer into the lives of the people onscreen.

During his first weeks at Columbia, Frank Capra became used to the bellowing and belligerent nature of Harry Cohn. He had seen similar people growing up on the streets of Los Angeles and he knew instinctively how to deal with them. It was not so different from his days selling the *Los Angeles Times* as a young boy. You had to throw the first punch and never back down.

One day, when Frank ordered thirty extras for a scene and half that number showed up, he stopped shooting and walked to Cohn's office. He refused to be put off by Dorothy, the secretary, and demanded to be buzzed into the inner sanctum. Frank stalked in, slammed his fist on Cohn's desk, and said, "I ordered thirty extras. You gave me fifteen. Where are the rest?"

Cohn didn't miss a beat. "That's the way we do things here."

Frank slammed his fist on Cohn's desk and roared, "Next time I'll order sixty if I want thirty. Just so I know!" He turned on his heel and stamped out.

Because Cohn was an autocrat, he respected others who wanted control. He understood that Frank not only wanted control, he also knew how to run a set responsibly, and he did it within a budget. Moreover, audiences seemed to respond to his work. Cohn knew a good thing when he saw it and gave Frank the control he sought, as long as he turned a profit.

Joseph Walker, initially skeptical about Frank's youth and inexperience, was impressed with his energy, his lively interest in the technical aspects of filmmaking, and his willingness to listen to new ideas. Frank was young, but he knew how to be a leader. He kept the pace of the workday flowing and approached the work with enthusiasm and a bright, infectious energy that reminded even the most jaded workers of the fun and passion in making movies.

Cohn offered Frank a contract for five more pictures, with a raise. Frank agreed on the spot and made *So This Is Love?*, *The Matinee Idol*, *The Way of the Strong*, *Say It with Sables*, and *The Power of the Press*, all completed during 1928 in roughly six-week increments. He worked at a furious pace, never showing tension or the pressure he felt to cast or crew. All five films were commercial successes. Frank grew used to the way Cohn ran Columbia. With each successive film, Cohn's grudging respect for Capra grew.

Cohn gave Frank a loan so he could move out of the Hollywood Athletic Club and buy a house in Malibu, near the beach. Frank moved there with his friend, the actor Al Roscoe. Roscoe was also recovering from a divorce to an actress.

Frank's work pace left precious little time for a social life or for entertaining. However, he had a new confidence, born of the success he had experienced at Columbia. Every day was shaped by the grueling schedule of film shoots, meeting the inevitable changes and emergencies with grace, and finally taking delight in the unexpected magic they created. Frank came to realize that filmmaking combined science, technology, leadership, and artistry in a delicate balance. It brought together all of the interests he had been cultivating all of his life up to that point.

Frank asked for Cohn to give him "A Frank Capra Production" credit above the titles of the films he directed; Cohn agreed. Frank began to wear tailored suits, silk shirts, and tuxedos made to order for premieres. He took great pride in his appearance. Young women and especially actresses, who abounded at Columbia, began to take notice.

Frank was attending a premiere at Grauman's Chinese Theatre on a balmy night in June 1928 when he saw Harry Cohn gesturing to him from across the plaza. One of Cohn's assistants elbowed through the crowd and said, "Harry wants to meet you in the screening room at Columbia in fifteen minutes." Frank took his date to her apartment, apologized, and hurried to the studio.

Cohn was already seated in the dark room, watching rushes from the first days of work on the shoot for *Submarine*. Directed by Irving Willat, it was by far the biggest-budget film Columbia had ever attempted. Jack Cohn and the East Coast office were breathing down Harry's neck every moment, and Cohn was on high alert. When Frank walked into the screening room, Cohn said, "I don't need to ask your opinion of this. It stinks. Audiences won't sit for it. I can't. I want you to take over on Monday."

Frank was momentarily stunned. He had never directed anything of this scope. He had not even read the script. But a day and a half later, on Monday morning at 6:00 a.m., he was riding to San Pedro in a Columbia limousine. *Submarine* was being shot in the harbor. It was a sailor buddy film starring two veterans, Jack Holt and Ralph Graves. The cast and crew, including Joseph Walker, were assembled when he stepped out of the limousine. Some looked concerned. Others, like Jack Holt, looked downright angry.

Frank knew he had to set the tone immediately. He stood on a piling as the sun rose over the San Pedro harbor. No one made a sound. Seagulls swooped after bits of food and bobbed on the waves. They, too, seemed to be waiting to hear what Frank Capra would say.

He took in the gathered crowd. He saw Joseph Walker's familiar face and thought he recognized a flash of encouragement.

"Now, I know some of you are worried, and I want you to know a few things," he began. "We are starting over." He turned to the crew and said, "We are going to work quickly and efficiently to make up for lost time." He turned to the actors. "You are going to take off every bit of makeup; no pancake, no eyeliner, no hairpieces, nothing. And muss up your uniforms. You've been at sea for weeks, not at a fancy resort."

Jack Holt was furious and stomped away. He put in call to Harry Cohn, who told him, "Holt, if you don't do exactly what Frank Capra says, I'll see to it that you never set foot on any set ever again."

When Holt returned to the set, Frank flattered him, saying that his acting talent would supersede the need for makeup and hairpieces. Holt was soon won over, along with the entire cast and crew, who warmed to Frank's leadership and friendly, unassuming manner. Frank was calm and never seemed to get upset. But he also knew exactly what he wanted and was able to communicate it to everyone.

He used his engineering expertise and sheer imagination to shoot a deep-sea diving scene with an aquarium and toy diver he bought at the Gower drugstore. He placed sodium in the diver's helmet to create bubbles that looked mysterious and utterly realistic.

Another crucial aspect of *Submarine* was the use of sound effects. Frank Capra, with his interest in science and technology, had heard Al Jolson sing in *The Jazz Singer*, which came out the year before. Frank fully embraced sound and understood the implications of its capabilities. Because of the initial lack of equipment, there was a scramble among the studios for microphones, recording devices, and ways to make the technology less cumbersome to the filmmaking process. *Submarine* includes a sequence in which Jack Holt, diving underseas, taps on the window of a submarine to see if anyone is alive. He hears a faint tap in return. Audiences were thrilled.

Submarine also cemented Frank's partnership with Joseph Walker. Frank encouraged Walker to use his zoom lenses, variable diffusion lenses, and optical diffusion lenses, and to experiment with them while shooting. The success of *Submarine*, and the manner in which Frank Capra had stepped in, vaulted him to one of the top directors at Columbia.

The Younger Generation, filmed in 1929, interwove silence with partial sound. The theme of the film, escaping one's past, reflected Frank's own deep-rooted conflicts about his immigrant family. The film also warned of the potential isolation and enslavement of material wealth. Morris, an upwardly mobile young man, is eager to escape poverty and the ghetto of Jewish life on the Lower East Side. In one painful sequence, he pretends to a wealthy friend that his parents are servants. Morris is ultimately rejected by his own mother, who prefers the community and warmth of the Lower East Side to the loneliness and coldness of her son's Fifth Avenue mansion. The final scene, with the rich but friendless Morris staring at the fire, slats of a shade falling across his shoulders like prison bars, is a stark and powerful reminder of the perils inherent in a focus on material wealth.

This theme resonated with Frank Capra as he became more successful. The desire to become a part of the American dream while recreating its joys and perils on film became a central aspect of his work.

By the end of 1929, Frank had proven his worth to Columbia Pictures. Although the country had plunged into the beginning of a depression that would last, in some form, for the next decade, he was earning $25,000 a picture. As a director who could tell stories visually with humanity and specificity, he was nearly indispensable to his employer. He had formed a creative partnership with Joseph Walker, a cinematographer who gave grace, depth, and beauty to his work. Although Frank Capra clashed often with Harry Cohn, together they had achieved financial success for Columbia Pictures. Now they shared another common goal: They both wanted the respect of the Hollywood community. There was only one ultimate symbol for that: an Oscar.

Chapter Six

THE EMBRACE OF LOVE

"What are you eating?" Frank asked. He directed his question at a petite, dark-haired woman with large brown eyes. She'd just taken a bite of something. She was sitting at an elegant dinner table, and Frank had arrived at the dinner late.

The shooting day for the film *Flight* had gone long. Jack Holt, the star, was drunk again. Frank had allowed the scene to be shot although Holt slurred his words. He planned to show it to Holt the next day. Maybe if Holt saw himself in that condition, he would stop drinking before work. The location, near San Diego, was in a flight pattern, and Ed Berends, Frank's soundman, had to stop constantly for sound. Sam Briskin was on the phone nonstop about costs. It was a typical day.

Frank regretted accepting an invitation to go out for dinner with a crowd from the shoot. After work, he rushed back to the Hotel del Coronado, where he was staying. He showered and put on his best suit. It was a little formal for the occasion, but everything else he owned was at the dry cleaners. There was a message from Ginger Rogers. They were dating. Every man in America wanted to date Ginger Rogers. And here he was, Frank Capra, the little boy from Bisacquino, dating one of the most sought-after actresses in Hollywood.

Ginger herself acknowledged the difference between reality and the legend created by Hollywood publicists. Once, when Frank and Ginger were leaving Schwab's drugstore, Ginger picked up a fan magazine with her picture on the front. She turned to Frank and said, "Gee, I wish I looked like that." That was Ginger. She was funny, self-deprecating, charming.

They met at a party Al Roscoe threw at the house in Malibu. Frank admired Ginger immensely. He loved her beauty, her grace, her sense of humor, her talent. There was only one problem. Ginger Rogers was an actress. Frank had vowed never to marry another actress.

Unlike many men in Hollywood, Frank genuinely respected and admired actresses. In his nearly ten years in the business, he had seen the combination of vulnerability and grit these women had to have to survive. He was grateful for the intensity and passion they brought to their work. He had begun to develop methods to understand how each individual actor was able to bring herself or himself to their roles. Actresses were often called upon to be emotional one moment and tough as nails the next. Their success in doing so believably became his success. He protected them and tried to bring out the best in their work.

In many of the actresses Frank came to know, he saw the same kind of resilience he had seen in his mother, Sarrida. He found her steeliness and toughness inspiring, and he loved seeing these qualities in the actresses he directed. He just didn't want to be in love with any particular one.

At the same time, he was growing weary of the bachelor life. The parties Al Roscoe and his friend, the actor Wallace Beery, threw at the Malibu house were growing tiresome. Frank wanted more. The Sunday before coming to San Diego for *Flight*, he'd watched a family on the beach in front of his house. The father swung his delighted son out over the waves while the mother built a sandcastle with her daughter. Inside Frank's house, it was martini time. Actors and starlets swirled through the rooms laughing and drinking. Suddenly, to Frank, it seemed hollow. He yearned to be that family on the beach.

Now he found himself at the end of a long table at the Chart House Restaurant in Coronado. Dinner had already been eaten and dessert was sitting on the table.

"It's a Kadota fig," said the young woman, answering his question. Her voice was low and silvery, and she giggled a little while she said, "If there is anything you'd like to know about Kadotas, or any fig, I can tell you because my father grew them on his ranch. You look hungry, by the way. You missed dinner."

She raised her hand to signal a waiter. Frank noted she wore no ring. A waiter appeared.

"How do you like your T-bone?" she asked, then turned back to the server without waiting for a response. "Medium rare for the gentleman, and a lettuce wedge light on the blue cheese," she said.

The waiter hurried off. She turned to Frank with a grin.

"Okay. I just guessed. How'd I do?"

Frank said, "Brilliantly. Just perfect."

"If you can't finish any of it, I'll eat it. By the time it gets here, I may be hungry again. I've got a big appetite," she said.

"It doesn't show," said Frank admiringly.

"Well, I'm wearing an A-line skirt and a schoolmarm blouse. I don't know if I could squeeze into one of those bias-cut, low-necked things like they're wearing." The young woman nodded her head toward two impossibly thin young women at the end of the table. "I don't worry about every bite I eat," she said, "although Kadotas are a perfect diet food."

She finished off the delicacy and licked her fingers. "You'll have to excuse my cretinish behavior. I don't get out much. And I used my napkin to wrap up a piece of chocolate cake for later. Shhh." She put her fingers to her lips.

"As to what you are wearing, sometimes it is more alluring to leave things to the imagination," said Frank. "By the way, I am—"

"Oh, I know who you are, silly. Everyone does. I've been a fan since *Submarine*, and I'm ashamed to say I read all the magazines. Is Ginger Rogers as beautiful in real life as she is onscreen?"

Frank ignored the question. "Well, I don't know you, but I'd like to."

"I'm Lucille Warner Reyburn. Reyburn is my married name, and everyone calls me Lu. You can, too."

Frank's heart sank a little. She was married. He looked away, and they sat in silence for a few moments. When his steak came, he wasn't very hungry.

"Dig in, Frank," Lu urged. "It's going to get cold. And I can feel my hunger setting in."

"Is your husband on the shoot? I thought I knew everyone," asked Frank.

Lu's cheerful demeanor dropped and she said, slowly, "No, he passed away. But let's not talk about that now. I'm a guest of your second assistant director. They insisted I come to get me out and about. I've been sort of a hermit."

"Are you an actress?" Frank had to ask.

"Heavens, no. I'm a secretary for a real estate firm in Los Angeles. I've been sequestered for awhile, living with my parents, and my friends wanted to get me out of my . . . out of my grief, I guess, and so they invited me down here. The grief never goes away, it seems to subside on some days. But I love movies!" she said, brightening. "They've saved me during this time. I sneak away and get lost in them. I appreciate them and all of you." She indicated the group at the table, eagerly talking shop. "I just want to admire you from afar."

They talked for hours, until the band in the restaurant stopped playing and the waiters had cleared all the tables. They stood up at the same time and walked together toward the door.

"Could I offer you a ride home?" asked Frank.

"You're lucky I'm not going back to Los Angeles," Lu said. "I'm staying at the Hotel Del."

"So am I," said Frank, "but I would have driven you anyway." A valet ran off to retrieve his car.

"I'd never let you drive me all the way back to Los Angeles," Lu said. "But I'd love a ride to the Hotel Del. You've got to be on set early, right? I have strong convictions about these things. I'm descended from Sir Thomas Moore, you know."

"Impressive," said Frank. "I like rock-solid convictions in a woman. Too bad Sir Thomas's life turned out so tragic."

"Tragedy has a way of sneaking up on you," said Lu, getting into the passenger side of Frank's Peugeot.

Frank couldn't help noticing how lovely she was; her slim ankles, and the way her hair curled around her ear. He found her voice soothing and comforting as she told him about her family, ranchers from a small California town named Warnerville, after her grandfather. They drove down the road, which meandered around the Strand beach and followed San Diego Bay. The windows were down and they could hear the waves washing up on the shore. The stars glistened on the horizon, and it seemed as if they were the only two humans alive. Everything else fell away.

It was a night for telling secrets. "I was an English major at Berkeley but left after two years," Lu said. "I met my husband shortly after. He was in the oil business. I loved him so." She paused. "He died suddenly, of a burst appendix when peritonitis set in. Some days I still can't believe he is gone."

Frank nodded sympathetically. Then he told Lu the story of his father's death. He had never told anyone about it. Now he unburdened himself of every detail. When he came to the part about seeing his mother prostrate on the floor of the pump house, he broke down. He had to stop the car. His shoulders heaved and he couldn't get control of himself.

Lu put her arms around him. There was no sound but his

sobbing and the crash of the waves. The moon shone over the bay.

A slight breeze ruffled the bougainvillea that clung to the white adobe walls of the Hotel Del. Dew had fallen on the stone path that led to Lu's cottage. Frank held her elbow. Her skin was soft and warm to the touch. He thought of Isabelle Daniels, of Helen, of the women in between; then they fell away. He had no hesitation. They kissed. Something inside Frank broke apart and he felt lighter, easier. They said good night and Frank began to walk away.

Lu ran after him. "I'm giving you half the piece of chocolate cake. Doctors say you should always have something sweet before sleep."

"No, they don't," said Frank with a laugh.

She kissed his cheek and thrust the napkin with the cake into his pocket. "Well, Doctor Lu does."

Flight premiered at Grauman's Chinese Theatre on September 13, 1929. It was the first Columbia film to premiere at Grauman's. Its success crowned Frank Capra as the star director at Columbia.

With the advent of sound, every studio began searching for writers to create stories and dialogue. Talent scouts scoured Broadway for playwrights and newspapers for journalists. The restrictions and budgets at Columbia demanded that stories had to be extremely well crafted and realistic, as they had no scenery, action sequences, or musical numbers to disguise mediocre writing.

Harry Cohn began hiring writers who could imagine stories that would appeal to mass audiences. He especially valued witty, realistic dialogue that felt natural and created worlds audiences could believe in. He stocked Columbia with a group of writers who could produce prodigiously and economically. Many had come from backgrounds similar to his own, hardscrabble immigrants raised on the Lower East Side of New York. In this arena, as well as others, Cohn had a knack for finding and hiring some of the best in the business. His hiring tactics for writers were no different than for actors or crew. He would berate and belittle their former work, then sit back to see how they reacted.

One such writer was Jo Swerling. A Jewish refugee from the Ukraine, he grew up on the Lower East Side. Like Frank Capra, he spent his childhood selling newspapers. Swerling began writing for newspapers and magazines in the 1920s. He wrote the Marx Brothers' first film, an unreleased silent comedy. His greatest success before coming to Columbia was *The Kibitzer*, a play he co-wrote with Edward G. Robinson that had a respectable run on Broadway.

Swerling suffered no fools and passed Cohn's hiring test easily. He was present, on his first day of work, in a story meeting where a script Frank had written was being discussed. Frank's position at Columbia was such that most people in the room praised it effusively, hoping to curry favor.

Swerling's opinion was the last. He pulled no punches. "It's terrible. Just awful. From start to finish. I could rewrite the entire thing, and make it work, in a weekend."

Rather than being offended, Frank was curious and welcoming. He invited Swerling to do what he said he could do. Swerling rewrote the script and it became the film *Ladies of Leisure*. Swerling soon became known, even among the prodigiously talented writers at Columbia, for his ability to write and rewrite with speed, alacrity, and brilliance.

Ladies of Leisure was a huge departure for Frank from the big-budget action film *Flight*. It concerned a young woman, a prostitute, who falls in love with a wealthy painter. His family rejects her, a now familiar theme. Swerling crafted a script that created characters with depth and evoked great empathy for the leading character. It was now up to Frank to cast the role.

Frank had begun dating Lu seriously. His interest in other women had fallen away, but the experience of his first disastrous marriage prevented him from taking the leap.

While Frank was casting *Ladies of Leisure*, a young actress came to Columbia to interview for the lead. Cohn had marked her as someone who was just beginning in film but who had potential. In other words, he could get her cheaply. He suggested Frank meet her.

She entered Frank's tiny office with a sullen "Hello." She was smoking a cigarette. Her dark hair hadn't been combed. She wore a striped cotton shirt, brown skirt, and sensible shoes. She slouched in the chair across from Frank and propped her head in the palm of one hand.

"We'd like to do a test of—" Frank began, assuming she wanted to get right down to business.

"I'm not doing a test," she answered, cutting him off and waving at a fly that was climbing the wall. She took a drag of her cigarette and blew out the smoke in a ring.

Frank began again. "I need a test so my cameraman, Joe Walker, can—"

The young actress abruptly stood up, and Frank realized how tiny she was. She leaned over Frank's desk and said, "Look here. I'm not making one more damn test for you or for anybody. I'm sick of tests, I'm sick of this town, and I'm sick of people like you. I know how to act. I've been doing it since I was fourteen, and I'm going back to New York where there are real people. I have nothing to offer Hollywood and I hate it, see. I hate it!"

She stubbed out her cigarette in an already full ashtray. Butts fell to the floor. She stomped out of the office. Frank could hear her clattering down the stairs. He thought he had seen the last of her. Harry Cohn called Frank later that day. "How did Barbara Stanwyck work out?"

"Terribly," replied Frank. "She's not an actress. She's a porcupine."

The same day, Frank received a call from Frank Fay, who said he was Barbara Stanwyck's husband. Out of curiosity, Frank accepted the call.

"I'm sending over a filmed scene from Barbara's Broadway triumph, 'The Noose,'" Fay said. "You've got to take a look."

"Look, Fay, she doesn't seem to want the job," said Frank.

"You're wrong about that, and you'll never find another girl who can do what she does. Just take a look," Fay pleaded.

If nothing else, Frank Capra was impressed by the man's faith. He promised he would, then immediately forgot his promise in the maelstrom of the day. Just as he was about to leave that evening, a harried messenger dropped off a package on Frank's desk. Inside was a film reel and a handwritten note that read, "When you see this, you'll understand." It was signed Frank Fay.

Frank went to the screening room and began watching the film. It was crudely shot, but the emotional power was unmistakable. Frank believed utterly in the despair of the life being portrayed and the will to rise above it. He had found his lead for *Ladies of Leisure.*

From her first day on the set, Frank was deeply impressed by Barbara Stanwyck. She came completely prepared and knew every line as written. She was able to turn on a dime emotionally and convey the toughness, humor, and vulnerability of Kay Arnold, her character, with utter sincerity. She worked well with the other actors and seemed to have no ego. Moreover, after the first few days, she knew the names of everyone on the set. Frank heard her asking after their spouses and children.

They rarely discussed things like character motivation; Frank could feel that Barbara didn't need that. Instead, they had long talks about how the scenes fit into the story as a whole. The work always proceeded from the notion that they were all in it together. Frank never said, "This is what I want." He always spoke of the work as what "we" want. In this way, the cast and crew felt that each person had a vital part. They all understood it to be something everyone was contributing to, and Frank's warmth and inclusion promoted this feeling.

After the first few days with Barbara, Frank realized that because she was from the theater, she tended to give all she had on the first few takes. She didn't know how to save emotions for future takes. Frank set up more than one camera to capture her from all angles. He made it clear to Joe Walker, the cameraman, and the other crew that they were there to serve the actors, not the other way around.

Frank was empathetic to the emotional strain and hard work of the actors during the grind of shooting a film. He did everything he could to assist them in creating naturalistic, unaffected performances. For example, he kept a nail in his pocket. If an actor forgot their lines or was otherwise struggling, he would drop the nail to create a disturbance and give the actor time to recover without embarrassment. This kind of thoughtfulness endeared him to actors.

Barbara Stanwyck was no exception. She blossomed during the filming and Frank could see that she was going to be a major star. He found himself thinking about Barbara all the time, whether he was at the studio working with her intimately or away at dinner with Lu. He was careful to describe his work on *Ladies of Leisure* as a step above, due to Jo Swerling's script and the work of the other actors. When Ed Berends was called in to work on the film as a replacement for the previous soundman, he immediately felt that the work going on was something special. They were shooting at Malibu Lake. The set had a calmness, sense of purpose, and camaraderie that was unusual and inspiring. Berends vowed to work with Frank Capra as much as possible.

A scene of which Frank was especially proud was the one where Jerry Strong, the wealthy painter, brings Kay Arnold, the lady of leisure played by Barbara Stanwyck, back to his apartment to paint her. They stand on the verandah looking at the sky and he exhorts her to look up at the stars, not down. He is inspired by her beauty and charm. She stays overnight because it is late. He makes up a bed for her in the studio. Their longing for each other is expressed through furtive glances. Rain falls; Frank loved using rain as an effect. The painter, played by Ralph Graves, lovingly wraps a blanket around the young woman. His kindness touches her. She bites the edge of the blanket. In a series of artful and silent shots, their desire and growing love are portrayed.

As Frank watched the rushes the next day, he realized he had done what he vowed not to do. He had fallen in love with another actress. He had Lu, but Barbara's talent, capabilities, and strength combined to mesmerize him.

Frank and Barbara shared many traits in common. They both came from tough childhoods. Barbara was orphaned at age four and shuttled among foster homes. She became a chorus girl at sixteen, working at the Strand Theatre and the New Amsterdam Theatre in the Ziegfeld Follies. Her breakout performance had come in a Broadway play, *The Noose*. It featured a character she became known for portraying: someone who endured tragedy but became more resilient and alive because of that experience.

Barbara had met and married Frank Fay, a charming and successful vaudeville performer. He was known even then to be an alcoholic. His erratic behavior only increased, with dire consequences in both his professional and private life. Despite emotional and even physical attacks, Barbara remained fiercely loyal to Frank Fay. Her loyalty and honesty were her trademarks as a person, in addition to her almost total lack of pretension. Both on and off camera, Frank found these qualities irresistible.

Frank and Barbara also shared similar political convictions. Barbara was a Republican who strongly believed in the rights of the individual and disagreed with government intervention. She felt that she had pulled herself out of the gutter by herself and others could, too. Frank had never met anyone quite like her.

On the evening when soundman Ed Berends was called to Malibu Lake, Barbara was filming a scene where she was rowing a boat away from a rowdy party. It was cold but she was, as usual, uncomplaining. The filming was halted while they waited for Berends to arrive.

Frank stopped by Barbara's trailer and found her alone and sobbing, her head on her dressing table. She didn't hear Frank knock. Her sorrow seemed to encompass her whole being. She looked up and said, "I am so sorry! I'll fix my makeup and come right to the set."

"No, no, they have stopped for at least half an hour. Put something on. You are freezing to death in that thin dress." Frank grabbed a flannel robe and stopped short. There was a huge bruise on her back and another on her arm.

Barbara said quietly, "How incredible that I should have two Franks in my life. One who pushed me down the stairs last night, and one that is so kind, so good to me."

She broke down again, and Frank put his arms around her. He kissed her, knowing he was breaking his cardinal rule. Despite the fact that Frank Fay was a loathsome character, he felt guilty about the fact that she was another man's wife. There was also Lu.

They finished the film and it premiered April 5, 1930. Audiences loved Barbara Stanwyck, as Frank had predicted. She became an immediate star. Through the shoots for *Rain or Shine* and *Dirigible*, Frank's next two films, they continued to see each other, with increasing guilt.

Frank had met Myles Connolly, an author, screenwriter, and fellow Republican, as well as a devout Catholic, at the wrap party for *Ladies of Leisure*. The friendship between the two—Myles, a large, clumsy, bear-like man and Frank Capra, economic, small of stature, and full of energy—had grown. They shared a love of literature and intellectual pursuits, reading, philosophy, and, increasingly for Frank, Catholicism.

Connolly had been educated at Boston Latin School and Boston College. His sister was a nun. He was deeply religious and conservative. He and Frank shared a dislike for Franklin D. Roosevelt and all he represented, particularly his thoughts about the New Deal and how to wrest the country out of the Depression.

Connolly began to question Frank about his work as a director. "Besides money, why do you do it, Frank?"

"I do it because I love every minute of it. I love the planning of it, the execution of it, the problem solving of it. I love feeling people sit there in the dark and enjoying it; I love seeing them lose themselves in it and forget their troubles."

Myles gave Frank a laconic stare. "Don't you think you have a greater responsibility than that?"

"I have a responsibility to Harry Cohn and Columbia Pictures and all the people who work there and depend on these films to make a living, and to A. P. Giannini at the bank to pay off the loan on the house we are standing in, the house we are having this very party in, the house you love to come to on the beach in Malibu. How's that?" said Frank.

"Seriously, Frank. To the thousands of people sitting out there in the dark, what is your responsibility? You've got them captive. Read my book, *Mr. Blue*, and tell me what you think," said Myles.

Al Roscoe bore down on them, "We have to separate you two. Way, way too serious," he said, offering them a tray of cocktails.

Frank bought *Mr. Blue*, Myles Connolly's book. It was the story of a modern-day St. Francis, a man who is wealthy but gives it all away to live in a packing box. He befriends other poor and disenfranchised people and decides to explore what it would be like to truly live his religion, to take into account what God asks of humankind.

Mr. Blue made a deep impression on Frank and affected him for the rest of his life. He realized that he was no longer interested in making movies that just entertained. He agreed with Myles Connolly that he owed something to the public that clamored for the films he made. He began to feel that with great power comes great responsibility.

Frank and Barbara Stanwyck continued to have intense feelings for each other. But Barbara remained loyal to her husband, Frank Fay. Frank Capra went so far as to invite Barbara to the house on Odin Street one evening. She charmed Anne and Sarrida by insisting on washing the dishes and sweeping the kitchen floor.

"I'm in love with her too, Frankie," said Sarrida, "but she's already taken."

Encouraged by Myles Connolly, Frank found a subject he felt was worthy: corruption in religion. With religious leaders like Aimee Semple McPherson in the news, the story of a young woman evangelist who teams up with a con artist and finally breaks free was attractive to Frank. He prepared a pitch for Cohn and the assembled Columbia writers in September of 1930. They listened intently as Frank spun the tale of *The Miracle Woman*, gesticulating and moving all around a cramped office on the Columbia lot to emphasize certain plot points.

Halfway through the pitch, a slender, distinguished-looking man in horn-rimmed glasses and a brown silk suit slipped into the back of the room. He leaned against the wall, smoking a cigarette and listening with his handsome head cocked to one side. When Frank was finished, the man spoke up in a quiet but decisive voice.

"I recognize all of that," he said. "It's based on a play I wrote with John Meehan. It ran on Broadway, but not for long. I can tell you why. It didn't work with audiences then and it won't work with audiences now. It's leaden. Too heavy. The overlay of message is too strong. They didn't buy it there and they won't buy it here. Sorry to be the bearer of bad news. But look at the bright side. I've just saved you a lot of headache."

"I think there is an audience of people who want to see a character reject money and greed for integrity," Frank insisted. "They want to see a person save her soul and her honor."

"I'm telling you it's moralizing and heavy and they won't buy it."

Frank stiffened. He was determined that *The Miracle Woman* would be his next film at Columbia. His power at the studio was such that it would undoubtedly happen. But the man at the back of the room intrigued him.

"Okay, fair enough," Frank said. "But who are you and what are you?"

"I'm a screenwriter. Robert Riskin. Harry Cohn has hired me to work here at Columbia, so I guess you're stuck with me." Riskin laughed and took a long drag of his cigarette.

The Miracle Woman was made, and Riskin was right. It was not popular with audiences, although critics continued their love affair with Barbara Stanwyck.

One day in August of 1931, when Frank was working in his office, a woman appeared at his door. Behind her was the tiny, dusty courtyard and the fountain at Columbia that had never worked. It was used as an ashtray. The day was hot and all of the doors facing the courtyard were open.

The woman's face was hollowed-out and ravaged, yet somehow familiar to Frank. She stepped inside. She was rail-thin and leaned against the door jamb for support.

"It's Helen, Frankie. You look so handsome, so wonderful. I know you're famous now. You can't pick up a paper or magazine without reading about you. I know what you're thinking. You're thinking I came here because of that, because you're famous. But that's not why."

Her voice began to rise, and Frank could see curious heads in nearby offices begin to turn. They were always looking for some sort of distraction. Frank invited her in and closed his door.

"Look, Helen. You are a good woman and I always cared for you, but—"

"But nothing. I told you I couldn't have children. But I did. She's three years old. Miracles can happen, Frankie."

Frank stepped closer and saw how broken she was. He couldn't tell if she had been drinking or if she had stopped. The damage had been done for Helen and for everyone around her. He pitied her child. He said, with calm finality, "Helen, I'm going to walk off the lot with you. I'll arrange a ride for you wherever you need to go. Is there anything else you need? Are you all right with money?"

"I don't need anything from you Frank, except the one thing you can't give any woman. You're married to your work. You don't love anybody but you."

That night, Frank broke off his affair with Barbara Stanwyck.

"It's not right," he told her. "It doesn't work you or for me. We want different things. There is no actress I respect more. But I've decided I need to find a wife."

Barbara looked at him a long time, as if she were trying to memorize his face.

"Frank, you had faith in me," she finally said. "You gave me my first big break out here in this land of phonies. I love our work, what we've created together. It will never go away. I'm grateful to you, Frank. You have a wonderful woman who loves you. Lu wants to be your wife. A woman like that won't wait around forever."

In fact, Frank almost lost Lu. In 1932, he traveled to Europe on a vacation with Al Roscoe. He had not yet proposed to Lu; fear was still stopping him. Then he received a letter from Lu. It was gentle but clear. She had formed a new relationship with a Dr. Brown. She loved Frank, but as she wanted a marriage and a family, she had to move on.

Within twenty-four hours, Frank sent Lu a telegram proposing marriage. Lu traveled to New York to meet Frank on his return from Europe. It was pouring rain when he came down the gangplank and took Lu into his arms. The next day, on February 1, 1932, a Brooklyn judge who was an old friend of Harry Cohn's pronounced them man and wife. The rain came down in sheets as they made their way uptown to the Waldorf Astoria.

"It's raining dear, just as it does in romantic scenes in your movies," said Lu, looking up at her husband.

"This is no movie, honey," Frank said, kissing her. "This is real life. It's so much better."

In May 1930, immediately after completing *The Miracle Woman*, Frank began working on a film that eventually came to be called *Platinum Blonde*. It added luster to the blossoming career of Jean Harlow and made her a major star. She was miscast as a snobby socialite, and it took more than twenty takes for her to say the word "library" instead of "liberry." Nevertheless, Frank admired her unpretentious friendliness and her scrupulous work habits. She stayed on set even after her scenes were shot to learn as much as she could about acting. She was open and curious.

Frank was even more impressed with the work of Robert Williams, the male lead. His charm and effortless ease were endearing. But the best part of the film, for Frank, was the writing. The dialogue for *Platinum Blonde* was written by Robert Riskin. Harry Cohn had been right to hire him. Riskin's work was impressive, and so was his support of other writers, who often clustered around the front porch of his office on the Columbia lot and asked for help and advice. Riskin gave it freely and soon became a respected favorite among his peers.

Like so many other writers in Hollywood at the time, Riskin had come from a Jewish background on the Lower East Side. Born May 30, 1897, he dropped out of school at the age of thirteen, but not before spending his childhood sneaking into the vaudeville theaters that populated his neighborhood. He took notebooks and wrote down jokes and sketches. At fourteen, he began working for a textile manufacturer in Lower Manhattan. He learned an early lesson in pleasing the audience when his boss asked Riskin to write a love poem for him to present to a girlfriend. When it did not have the desired effect, Riskin was fired.

Riskin went to work for shirtmakers Heidenheim and Levy. They happened to own an interest in an early film company that was a subsidiary of the former Famous Players-Lasky Corporation. It was located in Florida, and they sent seventeen-year-old Riskin there to manage the operation. Riskin wrote and produced over 100 short family comedy films there called "Klever Komedies."

Riskin served in the navy during the first World War but was not sent to Europe. After the war, he returned to New York where, with his brother Everett, he became part of a circle of brash young writers and actors who lived and worked near the fabled Green Room Club, a fraternal organization for men involved in the dramatic arts. It was located at 19 West Forty-Eighth Street. The club offered drinks, housing, and the company of other aspiring artists.

Often hard up for money, Riskin began writing plays about people who had to scramble for a living. He was fascinated by the gulf between the rich and the poor. His father had always been a Democrat and was very active in politics and liberal causes. Riskin teamed up with a female writer, Edith Fitzgerald, who also became a serious love interest. They wrote several plays together. Riskin wrote *Bless You, Sister* about a corrupted evangelist. It was produced on Broadway by his brother Everett. It had a modest success but caught the eye of Harry Cohn, who was in New York City on a scouting trip for writers and new material.

Robert Riskin came to Hollywood in 1930 to work for Cohn and Columbia. He was thirty-three at the time and involved in a long-term love affair with Edith Fitzgerald, who also came to Hollywood and began working for MGM. They broke up soon after, and Riskin, who was slender, charming, witty, and stylish, became known as a genial playboy; an eligible and very desirable bachelor. He dated some of the most beautiful women in Hollywood, including a serious relationship with Carole Lombard, and was often seen in gossip columns and the pages of film magazines.

Riskin began working for Cohn, understanding the position of Columbia in the Hollywood pantheon and aware of Cohn's reputation. He was intelligent enough to know that the stable of writers Columbia had already attracted, along with the kinds of intimate, humane stories he was interested in telling, might be just the sort of situation in which he could excel.

By 1930, Cohn and Columbia Pictures realized that their future lay in attracting and holding great writers. Because Columbia didn't rely on musicals, huge action features, or glossy costume dramas, they put a premium on story and dialogue. Words became all-important at Columbia. Cohn relied on the writers, yet despised the fact that he needed them. The close proximity of the writers to one another at the relatively small studio, plus the leadership of Robert Riskin, allowed them to form a sort of phalanx against Cohn. Their combined sagacity, intellectual sophistication, wit, and rebellious spirit was a match for Cohn's crudeness and ultimate power. They battled on a daily basis.

At Columbia, actors and producers came and went. Cohn treated directors with grudging respect. Frank Capra was in a special category because of the success of his films. But even he had to stand up to Cohn every day. For example, Cohn was banned by Capra from visiting any of Capra's sets. Cohn also reserved a gruff respect for writers, admitting that writing was something he couldn't do.

Unsatisfied one day in 1930 with the lunch he had at the Brown Derby, Cohn hit upon the idea of building his own executive lunchroom at Columbia. When it opened, the only people who could dine there were those invited by Cohn. All of the writers dreaded getting invitations, and when they did, they often couldn't resist using the occasion to insult and ridicule Cohn. Betting, horse racing, and University of Southern California football were favorite topics of conversation.

Once a writer bet that Cohn couldn't spell Columbia. The writer won. Another time, Cohn expounded on his theory of assessing whether a picture was good or bad. "If my fanny stays still, it's good, but if my fanny squirms, it's bad." There was a pause. Then the famous wit Herman J. Mankiewicz, who had been warned not to upset Cohn, couldn't resist. "Oh, so you're saying the whole world is wired to Harry Cohn's ass?" Mankiewicz was fired on the spot.

Cohn loved juvenile humor and had a chair wired to deliver a small electric shock. When an unsuspecting person sat in the chair, Cohn would press a button and the person would jump up in terror and surprise. He pulled the trick on Frank Capra only once. Capra jumped up and tore the entire chair apart with his bare hands. Cohn had a new one made the next day.

The film *Platinum Blonde*, which premiered on October 31, 1931, was a purely commercial venture for Columbia to recoup the losses from *The Miracle Woman*. It became a sensation among American women, who copied Jean Harlow's hairstyle, and American men, who found her sex appeal irresistible. Riskin's urbane dialogue and ability to make simple moments, like falling in love, so universal and charming, set a new standard for Columbia films. The character Stewart "Stew" Smith, played by Robert Williams, seemed to be an amalgam, of sorts, of the insights and longings of Robert Riskin and Frank Capra. Edward Berends, the soundman for the film, could see immediately the affection Frank had for Riskin. Even though Capra was a staunch Republican and Riskin an avowed Democrat, they found the same things appealing and funny. It was the birth of a creative marriage that would produce some of the most profoundly moving and funny films ever made.

Frank's growing reputation in Hollywood had fueled his outright desire for an Academy Award. Stung by Cohn's comment that a romantic comedy could never win and that the Academy would only vote for something "arty," he set out to make a film that was deliberately beautiful to look at and handled a deep subject: miscegenation. *The Bitter Tea of General Yen* is an anomaly in every way from almost every other film Frank Capra made, with the exception of *Lost Horizon*.

The Bitter Tea of General Yen is the story of a young engaged missionary couple who run an orphanage in revolutionary China. Megan Davis, the young woman, is caught up in a coup and taken to the palace of General Yen, a warlord, for safe-keeping. He falls in love with her, and she gradually falls in love with the mysterious and poetic General Yen. Unwittingly, she helps his enemies to overthrow him. The final scene, in which General Yen drinks a cup of poisoned tea while Megan Davis holds his hand and declares her love for him, is gripping and full of yearning.

Frank insisted that Barbara Stanwyck play Megan Davis, even though Constance Bennett was initially slated for the role. Filming took place after Frank and Barbara had ended their affair, but the moody feeling of the film and the ill-timed love the two leading characters have for each other echoed their relationship.

The film was not a box-office favorite. Megan Davis and General Yen were from different cultures and different races. In 1933, the subject of miscegenation was still shocking to audiences. They did not want to see a white woman hold a Chinese man's hand and look lovingly into his eyes. But *The Bitter Tea of General Yen* remains a beautiful departure for Frank Capra and an elegy for a relationship that could not continue.

By the time the film premiered, Frank Capra had been married for almost a year. He and Lu had spent their honeymoon traveling to the Winter Olympics at Lake Placid. They had met Benny Rubin, an actor friend of Frank's from the early days at Mack Sennett's studio, on the train. Rubin couldn't afford a Pullman car, and the newlyweds let him sleep on the sofa in their drawing room. They realized their good fortune and felt the need to be generous.

The magnitude of Frank's fame as a film director was brought home to Lu as journalists and publicists followed them the entire trip. Frank was gratified and Lu accepted it as she did most things, calmly and with humor and a protective eye toward her new husband. Frank was forever grateful. He had never experienced such love, and it gave him a renewed sense of freedom and confidence.

When Frank returned to Columbia in March 1932, the nation was in the depths of the Great Depression. Bankers like A. P. Giannini, who had financed much of Columbia and who had thrown his estimable weight behind Harry Cohn, allowing him to overcome a takeover bid by his brother Jack, were either vilified or lauded. Giannini was the model for the leading character, a banker, in a script Robert Riskin had written called *Faith*. It told the story of a banker who gives out loans based on his faith in the character of the people he serves. A series of mishaps and criminal interventions leads to a bank run, which is ultimately stopped by the community, which decides to believe in the banker's essential humanity. Although warned against making a film about a good banker during the Depression, Cohn went ahead with production, based on the strength of Riskin's script. Cohn had fired the first two directors because he felt their work was lifeless and dull. He insisted that Frank Capra take over.

With only three days of preparation, Frank brought energy,

focus, and a new vision to the work. The first thing he did was to create a new set. He directed the actors to speak at a fast clip, to overlap one another, and to bring a new pace to the scenes. The actors began to come alive. Frank had noticed that onscreen, where images are so large, time slows down and audiences can get ahead of the story. When actors pick up their rhythms and speak more quickly, it brings a whole new energy to the work.

American Madness became a film that moved along, constantly surprising the audience, and felt natural to the way people speak and behave. Frank also responded to the brilliant structure and well thought out characters Riskin created. Frank believed that everyone who appeared onscreen, whether lead or extra, was vitally important and needed to have an internal rhythm and reason for being there. If he felt an actor didn't have it, he was out of ideas for them. No one was ever "just crossing" the street; they had to have a reason and a motivation and be leading a full life. This kind of specificity gave the film depth and a sense of reality.

Collaborating as director and writer on *American Madness* cemented the respect and working relationship between Frank Capra and Robert Riskin. It was one of the first times Frank worked on a film that dealt directly with an issue important to American life in the moment. In a very real way, the film addressed questions haunting the lives of every American. Like the creators of the film, Americans were divided about how to solve the problems they faced. Riskin believed in the proposals put forth by FDR; Frank believed in the conservative principals of individual freedom and independence from government interference. Frank was also heavily influenced by Myles Connolly and his exhortations to create work that made a statement. Although Capra and Riskin had opposing political beliefs, it is to their credit that they worked together closely. This may have added a kind of creative tension to their work.

Harry Cohn's gamble paid off; *American Madness* was wildly successful. Its themes—a character placed in an impossible situation from which he must extricate himself, and the strength of community—would repeat, in various ways, in the work of Capra and Riskin throughout the next decade.

Working on *American Madness* further solidified the professional relationship and friendship between Frank Capra and Robert Riskin. It was on *Lady for a Day*, based on a Damon Runyon story, that the partnership really took off. Riskin wrote the screenplay. The two men began a way of working that would remain in place for years. They searched for great stories from many sources. Capra often came up with visuals based on the story. They had long, detailed discussions, and often arguments, either on the lot at Columbia or at their hotel retreat in Palm Springs, where they secluded themselves to work on plots and characters. Riskin wrote in longhand on his yellow legal pads. They chatted back and forth, always keeping the spine of the story in mind.

Lady for a Day is a relatively simple story of Apple Annie, a poor, aging fruit seller, who has fooled her daughter, Louise, into thinking she is a wealthy woman. Louise has grown up in a Spanish convent. One day, Annie receives a letter from Louise saying that she is bringing her Spanish fiancé and his aristo-cratic father to New York City to meet her. Annie's friends, all grifters, card sharks, and street toughs, band together to pull off a subterfuge, presenting themselves as wealthy scions of New York society to fool Louise and her entourage.

The film marked the first true collaboration between Riskin and Capra. The words, the characters, and the structure came from the pen of Robert Riskin. Frank Capra brought them to life by casting actors who filled their roles with life and by creating a set that allowed them to do their best work. He put together a team of the brilliant cameraman Joseph Walker, Edward Berends on sound, and a whole crew of people who understood the story they were telling.

Frank's joy and passion were infectious. Acknowledging the people who live in the poverty-stricken parts of the city, the effects of the Depression, and the disparity between the rich and the poor, the film doesn't shy away from the heartbroken despair of the mother, played with depth and feeling by the actress May Robson, or the delight in skewering the pretensions of the upper class.

Lady for a Day set out some of the defining features that would appear in nearly all subsequent Riskin/Capra collabora-tions: the strong-minded working woman, the presence of the press and the importance of their judgments, the hero with an Achilles heel, and the appearance of crowds, or community, at essential moments to buoy or to validate the hero. Frank's youth spent around newspapers became a vital part of his creative life as an adult. The sense of community and community spirit marks these films as essentially American while acknowledging the power of the individual to arouse deep feeling in the community.

Lady for a Day was nominated for Best Picture, Best Director, and Best Screenplay. Frank was well on his way to achieving the status and acceptance within the Hollywood community that he had long sought. He was no longer a little boy outside the Jonathan Club selling newspapers. He was a member of the Academy and part of a community that was about to split apart in battles over labor and politics.

At the 6th Annual Academy Awards, in March 1934, his old friend Will Rogers opened the envelope for Best Director, glanced at it, and announced, "Come on up, Frank." Capra assumed that Rogers was referring to him. He felt, for a moment, that his time had finally come, and he was now going to be accepted into the highest ranks of the Hollywood hierarchy. But Rogers was referring to Frank Lloyd, who had won for *Cavalcade*. Capra had already begun his walk up to the podium before he realized that another Frank had won. He was humiliated beyond words.

Shortly before filming began on *Lady for a Day*, Lu Capra experienced a miscarriage. The year 1933 would be a mixed blessing for Frank and Lu. But the way was paved for blessings to come. Frank was firmly established as a director of substance and style. Harry Cohn was happy with the box office receipts and the fact that Frank and Riskin had given him what he had wanted for so long: recognition in the form of Oscar nominations. Frank had found a sublime life partner in Lu and a love that would sustain and protect him. In Robert Riskin, he had found a screenwriter whose interest in human behavior, desires, and dreams matched his own.

On March 20, 1934, Lu Capra gave birth to a healthy baby boy. The delighted new parents named him Frank Capra Jr. Lu proved to be as calm and loving with her baby as she was with her husband; she took to motherhood naturally. It was one of Frank's great joys to come home at night and hold his infant son. He had palpable dreams for this young American. Frank vowed to keep him safe and to give him all the things he never had.

Chapter Seven

THE EMBRACE OF ACCEPTANCE

"I don't want to be stuck in Siberia," the handsome man said. Frank heard "shtuck" and "shy-beria." It was 10:00 a.m. on a weekday in early September 1933. The handsome man was Clark Gable, who had been forced by Louis B. Mayer and MGM to come to Poverty Row for a meeting with a director who looked to him like a boy.

Gable slumped in a tiny chair in Frank's dingy office on the Columbia lot. He was so drunk he could hardly hold his head up.

"I'm not a free man. L. B. Mayer's mad at me, so he's punishing me. He's sending me to Siberia. Say, it's hot in Siberia. Do they have fans in exile?"

Frank took a deep breath and said, "Do you want me to tell you about 'Night Bus' or read the script yourself?"

Gable lurched forward unsteadily. His eyes were bloodshot. He had several days' beard growth. He reeked of whiskey. Gable snatched the script. He rolled it into a tube and put it to his eye as if it were a spyglass. He trained it on Frank and said, "I hear I'm gonna be stuck on a bus for this one. I'm a pawn. Just a damn pawn in a spat between Harry Cohn and L. B. Mayer. And now I'm stuck on a bus. Damn."

He staggered out the door and walked directly into a wardrobe rack being pushed through the courtyard. The shocked wardrobe supervisor stood staring at him.

"Whaddya know? They actually have costumes in Poverty Row!" Gable exclaimed, grabbing a fedora off the top of the rack. "I thought I'd have to provide my own."

Gable wove his way down the dusty path toward the guard gate. The fedora was cocked rakishly on the side of his head.

Frank had found the short story "Night Bus" in Cosmopolitan magazine when he was getting his hair cut in Palm Springs. Written by Samuel Hopkins Adams, it told of a poor painter and an heiress escaping her wealthy life for love. He and Riskin were searching for something for their next film. They pitched it to Cohn.

"No. No way in hell!" bellowed Cohn. "There are too many damn bus pictures already. It's the Depression, or haven't you heard? There's a Dust Bowl blowing in the Midwest. Damn stuff is everywhere and people are dying. Bonnie Parker and Clyde Barrow are killing people for sport. People want entertainment. Do you think we are going to drag them into theaters to see a movie about yokels on a bus?"

"Yes, I do," said Frank, "if Bob writes it."

"What do I pay you two for anyway?" said Cohn. "In fact," he screamed, leaning out of his window, "what do I pay any of you for? To smoke cigarettes and drink coffee all day? I don't hear one damn typewriter!" There was a moment of quiet. Then the clack of typewriters was heard throughout the courtyard.

Cohn sat back in his chair with a huff. "I'm telling you, bus pictures stink. Come up with something people want to see. If you can write something good about a damn bus, I'm a monkey's uncle. Now scram and see what you come up with. But if it stinks, I won't do it."

Riskin and Capra left Columbia and Hollywood and worked in their preferred way, at the LaQuinta Hotel in Palm Springs. LaQuinta was an oasis of beauty and an escape from the pressures of Hollywood. The two men worked at a table shaded by a white umbrella, chain-smoking cigarettes and laughing frequently. During the late afternoon, they rested from their labors in their adobe cottages or swam in a pool under the cerulean desert sky.

Riskin did all the writing. He wrote the dialogue, the scenes, and specific visuals with ideas for character development. Frank often came to their work sessions with lists of ideas and suggestions for Riskin. Most were unusable. But once in a while, he came up with something brilliant.

The two leads in "Night Bus" were a spoiled heiress, Ellie Andrews, and a down-on-his-luck painter from Greenwich Village, Peter Warne. They fall in love on a bus trip. She is running away from her father, who wants her to marry someone she doesn't love.

When Riskin finished the script, both were confident that it would work. Frank showed it to Myles Connolly, as had become his habit. Connolly unfailingly gave honest, incisive responses, always based on his belief that Frank's work should have a message. He didn't seem to take his own advice, as he was working on *Tarzan* films. Nevertheless, Frank had come to value his intellect and his erudition when it came to screenplays.

Connolly's response to "Night Bus" was that the audience would not empathize with a spoiled heiress or an intellectual avant-garde painter. "You've got to make these two characters that people will respond to," he advised.

It was crucial advice. Riskin did a rewrite making Ellie Andrews a character who wants to escape her stultifying life. He made Peter Warne a hard-bitten, cynical reporter who rediscovers his own vulnerability when he falls in love. The new version of the script incorporated a theme that permeated almost all of the Capra/Riskin films: the war between the classes. Frank had known many girls like Ellie Andrews during his time at Manual Arts High School. He related viscerally to memories of the behaviors of the rich and his own reactions to them. He remembered vividly the dinners at Anoakia and his own discomfort and ultimate disgust with the laziness and entitlement of the wealthy. The world of the hard-bitten newspaperman was also familiar to both Frank and Robert Riskin.

The script they brought to Harry Cohn was still titled "Night Bus." Cohn blustered, "Get the damn word 'bus' out of it and it's a go. By the way, I've got Clark Gable for the lead. He's been a bad boy at MGM and Mayer's punishing him by sending him to Poverty Row. He's not happy about it, and he usually plays a heavy, not a romantic lead in a comedy. But now he's stuck on a bus and I got him for half of what he's worth." Cohn chortled with glee. "I've found the actor. Now you two find me a girl to play the rich dame."

The script was sent to Myrna Loy, Margaret Sullivan, and Constance Bennett. They all turned it down. Cohn mentioned Claudette Colbert and Frank cringed, remembering the disastrous experience with her during *For the Love of Mike*. But that had been her first film. Since then, she had made several more.

Frank and Rifkin were becoming desperate, afraid that the script would get a bad reputation among actresses and that no one they wanted to cast would say yes. They decided to go to Colbert's home in person and plead with her. They bought flowers, chocolate, and champagne and showed up on the steps of her home in Beverly Hills. A maid opened the door and three small white yapping dogs ran out. Frank bent down to pat one dog. Another ran behind and took a bite out of the seat of his pants.

"I think he may have gotten more than my pants," said Frank. "I am actually bleeding."

"Well, don't drip on her snow-white carpet or we'll never get this movie made," replied Riskin.

They begged Colbert, who seemed to be busy packing for a trip, to consider doing the film. She was adamant that her answer was no. She was planning a vacation to Sun Valley in the near future. She was not interested in changing her plans.

She finally rolled her eyes and, in a tone that implied she knew the absurdity of the demand, said, "If you give me $50,000 and shoot it in four weeks, so that I can leave for Sun Valley on time, I'll do it. I want to see Harry Cohn's face when you tell him that," she said with a laugh. "Now good-night, fellas. Have fun on your bus. And I'll send Harry Cohn a bill for cleaning my carpet. You seem to have dripped something."

Harry Cohn said yes. It was something both Frank and Bob Riskin admired about Cohn; once he made a decision, he usually stuck by it. He had decided to produce *It Happened One Night*, which is how it had been retitled, and there was no going back.

Colbert signed on, however reluctantly. The strict time limit imposed by her demands, plus the budget of $325,000, kept things necessarily simple. This was something at which Frank excelled. He took it on as a happy challenge. His cheer, optimism, and detailed organization, plus the camaraderie of the crew, headed by Joseph Walker as cameraman and Ed Berends on sound, made the set a fun place to be. Frank's daily ebullience reminded them all of why they had gotten into the business in the first place.

Clark Gable, who was initially angry and recalcitrant, quickly realized that Frank appreciated his sense of humor and wanted him to just be himself. Used to being cast as sinister gangsters, Gable began to relax and enjoy the experience. As he did, his natural charm and magnetic personality came through. He allowed a kind of vulnerability that was touching and eminently relatable.

Claudette Colbert remained somewhat aloof and slightly unfriendly, but Frank capitalized on this attitude because it worked perfectly for the character. When she refused to undress during the Walls of Jericho scene, in which Ellie and Peter are preparing for bed, Frank made the best of it by turning it into a tease, believing that the more left to the imagination, the better. He used her underthings as a tantalizing symbol of what might lie behind the Walls of Jericho.

Frank had the idea for the hitchhiking scene one day while driving to the location to shoot the sequence. When Claudette Colbert refused to show her leg in order to do the scene, Frank quickly found a stand-in. When she saw the stand-in, she immediately changed her mind. "My legs are so much better than that," she declared. "I'll do it myself." Frank had to agree. No one would argue with the notion that Colbert had some of the best gams in Hollywood. He gladly shot the scene with Colbert.

The scene in which the passengers on the bus break into a spontaneous version of "The Daring Young Man on the Flying Trapeze" was done as an improvisation. When Frank suggested it, Colbert objected, stating, "How would everyone know all the words? It isn't realistic." Frank was always willing to listen to and consider any suggestions, no matter where they came from. If he thought they were good, he would use them. This attitude was part of what made his set so lively and welcoming. It made the cast and crew feel as though they were all part of something. Frank asked everyone to sing what they knew, to chime in at whatever part of the song they wished, or to simply listen and enjoy it. It became a treasured moment, bonding the entire cast.

It also exemplified one of Frank Capra's tenets of good filmmaking. He felt that for an audience, it was essential to have at least one or two moments in a film in which the cast can be seen doing something easy or even delightful, and the audience can just take them in and enjoy them. He also used a similar effect during moments of great despair or tragedy, placing the camera so the viewer can rest with the face and the emotion of the character and dissolve into them. Anything that distracted from the story or the natural behavior of the characters was anathema to Frank. For him, "arty" shots or camera moves that displayed technique for effect distracted from the story and called attention to themselves, taking the audience out of the world of the film.

It Happened One Night finished shooting in time for Claudette Colbert's Sun Valley vacation. As editing began, Frank and Robert Riskin began preparation on another film, *Broadway Bill*, a racehorse saga based on a story by Mark Hellinger. The story had its roots and theme, once again, in the struggle between the upper and lower classes. Frank's energy and optimism, and the mutual respect between the cast and crew, continued to endear him to the actors. Clarence Muse, an actor who worked on the film, marveled at Frank's composure during a rainstorm that threatened to ruin a day of shooting. Frank quickly changed the schedule to shoot some interiors and took the time to speak to the cast about the feeling for the upcoming scene.

No part was too small for Frank to consider important to the overall feel of the story. He treated all the actors as though they mattered equally. One cardinal rule that the crew understood while working with Frank Capra was that they were never to cut until they were told to do so, no matter what technical problems they encountered. Frank respected the need of the actors to establish a rhythm and find their moments; he considered it sacrosanct. The actors with whom he worked deeply appreciated this. They knew they would never be interrupted for technical issues. They saw firsthand that Frank had the capacity to understand their process as actors, however unusual it might be. And because they felt safe with him, they did their best work for him.

One evening in early November 1934, Frank was taken to Cedars-Sinai hospital with excruciating stomach pain. As he lay in the white room with the smell of bleach clinging to the sheets, he couldn't help thinking of the time he was punched as a child. He recalled the fear and terror of that moment on the streets of downtown Los Angeles. No one had been there to help. Now he was surrounded by groups of nurses and two doctors.

Harry Cohn had already put in a call, within an hour of Frank being admitted. He and his wife, Rose, sent flowers. The gigantic bouquet of red and white roses impressed even the nurses who were used to dealing with celebrities. Frank understood that a great part of Harry Cohn's concern was the potential loss of his star director and a meal ticket for Columbia. After Lu, who was pregnant with their second child, had a hasty conference with the doctors, Frank was whisked to an operating room.

Doctors found the remnants of an ancient burst appendix, the real source of Frank's pain and illness after serving in the army. As Frank struggled to come out of the anesthesia, he dreamed that he could hear the slap of the cards on his mother's kitchen table. He heard her friends cackling and calling him lazy and no good. It all came back to him. He was grateful to awaken with Lu looking down at him. She was always there, always full of love.

"How did I get so lucky?" he mumbled.

"Shhh, darling. You are tougher than an old mule. It's not luck. It's being stubborn," Lu said with a laugh.

"I guess Sarrida's potato peels did the trick," Frank answered groggily.

Returning home after the surgery, Frank was uncharacteristically lethargic. On some days, he was depressed and anxious. Friends came to visit, among them Max Winslow, a musician and composer who was married to Harry Cohn's sister-in-law. Frank and Max shared a love of fishing in addition to their creative pursuits. Harry Cohn continued to call daily to inquire about Frank's health.

One night, when Lu was six months pregnant with their second child, Frank rubbed lotion on her expanding stomach. The miracle of childbirth never ceased to amaze him. He could feel the child kicking and turning.

"He really wants out," said Frank.

"How do you know it's a he?" said Lu.

"The way he's kicking, he could go ten rounds with Joe Lewis," Frank said.

"Do you think he could make Harry Cohn stop bothering you?"

"Oh, yeah. He could stand up to His Crudeness. Easy. He's his mother's son. He can do anything he sets his little mind to," laughed Frank.

As Frank languished at home, a curious phenomenon began to take place. *It Happened One Night* had opened in 1934 to lukewarm reviews. The press didn't seem to be excited by the bus picture. But over the ensuing months, word of mouth began to build. Audiences started attending in droves; many people said that they had gone back multiple times.

Then a tidal wave of people went to see it. The film broke box office records at theaters nationwide and eventually became one of Columbia's biggest hits. When people saw Clark Gable take off his shirt, wearing no undershirt, sales of undershirts dropped. No one had predicted this, least of all Frank Capra. He knew there had been ease about making the film, and an unexpected pleasure in seeing Clark Gable come alive. In fact, *It Happened One Night* completely changed the trajectory of Gable's career. He became such a box-office draw that Columbia could no longer afford to hire him.

Now Frank lay on his bed in his house on Selma Avenue in Hollywood. In early December, 1934, he was still recovering from his operation. Christmas travels to Silver Lake in the High Sierra were being planned. Lu slept quietly beside him. Their six-month-old boy, Frankie, slept down the hall. By any normal standards, Frank Capra was now a wealthy man. He had saved his money and invested it wisely. He was able to provide a comfortable life for his mother and his sister, Anne. At age thirty-seven, he was grateful but restless; he was worried about what was happening in the world.

The labor union struggles with the newly formed Writers Guild of America and the Screen Actors Guild had opened up schisms in the Hollywood community that did not bode well for future unity. Frank found himself in the middle. He had recently been elected president of the Academy of Motion Picture Arts and Sciences. Many of his colleagues, especially writers, felt the Academy was in league with producers who wanted to cheat them out of what they deserved.

The Depression was ongoing, and Frank felt responsible for providing some relief, some hope to the people who were spending their hard-earned money to come and see the films he made. He wondered if it was enough just to entertain. Myles Connolly continually harangued him about making statements with his work.

Suddenly a stabbing pain tore through Frank's side. It was so intense that he nearly blacked out. He was aware enough to hear a siren in the distance. He thought, "Maybe that's for me." He was correct.

Frank woke up at Cedars-Sinai. He had been hovering near death for three days. His room was filled with bouquets. Get Well cards had been set out on the table nearby. Lu stood at the foot of his bed. Lines of exhaustion etched her pale face. One hand rested on her growing stomach. She walked around the bed, bent down slowly, and kissed his forehead.

"You've been asleep for a long time, my love," she said. "I was afraid I was going to lose you. But I asked God not to let me lose two husbands to peritonitis. It would be redundant, don't you think, dear?"

She paused, then her beautiful voice lowered and she said, "It wasn't easy getting down on my knees with a stomach as big as a beach ball, dear, but I did it. I . . . I prayed for you so long and so hard. And God answered my prayers."

Frank and Lu prepared cautiously for the 7th Academy Awards ceremony on February 27, 1935. Frank was still recovering and had lost twenty pounds. His tuxedo hung on him. He looked gaunt. Lu wore a large fur coat to conceal her pregnancy. "I look ridiculous," she said, "but I am not missing this for anything."

"Honey, remember last year?" said Frank, as their limousine pulled up at their door. "We will probably stay seated eating bad chicken cordon bleu and drinking too much wine. I've learned my lesson. They are going to have to say my name three times before I will stand up. And you know what? I am really not expecting it. I don't think I will hear my name. It's a romantic comedy, and let's face it, romantic comedies never win."

"I know that despite what you say, you want this so badly, Frank," said Lu. "And I want it for you. Just remember that whatever happens, we have each other."

It Happened One Night had been nominated for Oscars in five categories. Still, Frank and Lu Capra expected nothing when they entered the Biltmore Hotel in Los Angeles. Claudette Colbert wasn't even planning to attend. She was in the process of boarding a train at Union Station, wearing a plain brown wool traveling suit, when Best Actor Clark Gable was announced. An apoplectic Harry Cohn, sensing something good might happen, sent Columbia employees to fetch her. They brought her to the Biltmore just as her name was announced for Best Actress. She strode to the podium to accept her Oscar, made a short speech, looking astonished, then stepped away from the podium. She stepped back quickly and added, "I owe all of this to Frank Capra."

Frank saw his friend Robert Riskin win for Best Adapted Screenplay. Riskin made a characteristically witty and elegant speech. Frank sat at a table with Jo Swerling and his wife, Flo, Myles Connolly, Harry Cohn, Robert Riskin and, of course, Lu. When his name was announced as Best Director, it took a moment for it to register. Lu squeezed his hand. He stood up. A sea of applause broke out. It was as though he was walking through a dream.

It wasn't a dream. Frank found himself holding the statue, which was heavier than he had imagined. He looked out at the faces of so many colleagues who were looking at him expectantly. His throat constricted and he couldn't speak for a moment. He stammered out thank-yous to Gable and Colbert and Columbia Pictures. He felt himself lifted on the shoulders of his father, Turridu, gazing out at the lady in the harbor. They could never have imagined this dream. Not in a million years. But here it was.

Then the Oscar for Best Picture was announced. *It Happened One Night*. They had swept all five major awards, a feat that had never before happened to any film, let alone a romantic comedy. Harry Cohn stepped to the podium and, with uncharacteristic modesty, said, "I'm just an innocent bystander."

That night, Frank celebrated with friends Myles Connolly and the composer Dmitri Tiomkin and many others, drinking champagne and dancing on his front lawn at Selma Avenue until sunrise. Lu looked on with amusement and pride. Early the next morning, he awoke with a head that felt like a boulder. He heard the sound of bottles clanking against tin. Frank looked out his bedroom window and saw Sarrida, who had come to congratulate him, picking up empty bottles and tossing them into a garbage can. The racket made his head throb. Sarrida noticed him watching her. "Frankie, you gotta clean up," she scolded. "This doesn't look good."

On April 24, 1935, John Capra was born. The joy of his birth was clouded by the discovery that the infant had hearing loss and other delays that became more pronounced as the weeks went by. Doctors and experts were called in, but no one could put a finger on exactly what was happening. John was at times inconsolable, and Lu hired a nurse just to concentrate on him.

This was the 1930s, when people with disabilities were rejected and feared. Lu and Frank kept John's condition to themselves as much as they could and put on a brave face. But they were gravely worried about their son. Lu was strong and optimistic about his chances for growing out of his problems. Frank was, at times, depressed and anxious about his son.

Columbia Pictures, having swept the Oscars, was now firmly the contender that Cohn had always dreamed it would be. It could no longer be dismissed as a Poverty Row upstart. Frank shared this sense of pride, but also felt a constant pressure to match and even surpass what he had done with *It Happened One Night*. At times, he found himself burdened with a feeling of heaviness that drained his natural ebullience. Lu remained calm and strong, trying to understand her new baby and his needs while presenting a positive picture to the world. With great accomplishments came great expectations.

Frank Capra, at age thirty-eight, had climbed to the top of the mountain. But it seemed to him at times that there was no chance to enjoy the scenery. Harry Cohn kept up relentless pressure. There were now deep schisms in Hollywood between various factions within the newly formed writers, directors, and actors unions. Some union members felt it was their imperative to look outside Hollywood and address, or at least take strong stances on, world affairs. Others felt that the job of the union was merely to protect its members. With Fascism growing in Europe, a divide in America between isolationism and interventionism, and a burgeoning fear of communism, it was impossible for any individual to stay neutral.

Americans were going to the movies by the millions. Many were going several times a week. They looked to Hollywood to mirror their lives, to entertain them, and to take them away from their own struggles. They also looked to films to provide a context for hope. People longed to identify with heroes who had integrity and honor and in whom they could see something of their best selves.

Frank felt the weight of responding to this need. Not only had he been accepted by the public at large; he had also been acknowledged by his peers in the industry. He had proven himself invaluable to Columbia Pictures, and he knew that such a position is difficult if not impossible to maintain for long.

Frank was fine when he was making a film. Then his whole mind, his whole soul was so absorbed he couldn't think of anything else. He derived untold pleasure from playing with his son Frank and watching him grow. Lu was an unending source of love. But between films, when he was searching for a story to tell, darkness sometimes descended.

Old fears and insecurities came roaring back. Some days he was Frank Capra, an internationally known film director. And sometimes, late at night when he couldn't sleep and he wandered the hallways of his house on Selma, he would come face to face with the Oscar on the mantle. It comforted him. Its faceless visage also seemed to issue a challenge, as if to say, "I am blank until you bring me to life."

Chapter Eight

THE EMBRACE OF COMMUNITY

Frank and Lu Capra were dressed in their finest. The invitation from Carole Lombard had specified black tie. "I'd rather be puttering in my garden. Or playing with baby John," grumbled Frank.

"It's Bob Riskin's birthday, and Carole is his beloved girl-friend," Lu said. "We've got to go."

"When are they going to get married? All the gossip columns are urging it on," said Frank.

"Has he asked her?" answered Lu. "That might be a start. Darling, if I knew what made men tick, I'd be queen of the world."

"Well, you are queen of hearts: mine and Frankie's and little Johnnie's," Frank replied.

They had said goodnight to Frank Jr. and were standing over baby John's crib. He was asleep, sucking his thumb. His father patted his silky baby hair and looked down at him. Experts, doctors, and other specialists had examined him and tried to diagnose why he wasn't meeting developmental milestones.

Frank hated them all, hated the need for them, hated their poking, prying questions and pronouncements, but admitted they were necessary. Lu kept up a stoic optimism, a belief that he would eventually grow out of his problems with movement, speech, and regulation.

"We will just spoil him out of it," his father had declared more than once. Frank held him often, played with him, and tried to get him to respond as Frank Jr. did, as other children did.

Now he bent down to kiss his son.

"You've already kissed him three times, and you are going to wake him up," Lou said. "We are already late. Tear yourself away from your darling. He'll be here when you get home."

They arrived at Carole Lombard's, with Frank in a tuxedo and Lu in a silk dress, to find Lombard's Beverly Hills domicile filled with hay, ten mules, pigs, chickens, and a swimming pool complete with ducks. She had turned her elegant home into a barnyard, complete with a Western band. It was just like Carole to do such a thing: raise expectations for a fancy Hollywood party, then skewer them by filling her house with farm animals and hay bales. The guests accepted it with good humor and spent the evening dodging mule patties.

Frank and Lu joined their friends Robert Riskin, Sidney Buchman, Irving Thalberg and his wife, Norma Shearer, and a host of other celebrities in an evening of barnyard revelry. As the night went on and guests partook of Lombard's special punch and multiple cocktails, civilities began to go by the wayside, and the subject of politics came up.

Lombard tried to circumvent this by announcing early on

that anyone caught discussing anything serious would be tarred and feathered. But after midnight, guests ignored her request. Sidney Buchman taunted Frank by saying, "The Academy is nothing more than a bunch of shills for producers who want to fleece writers. How can you be president? They hate unions."

Thalberg wasn't going to let this stand. "They hate Communists. They hate anti-Americans. Let's get that straight."

Buchman shot back, "How do they feel about Hitler?"

"Hitler and Hitlerism will pass. Communism is a much more real threat to our democracy," answered Thalberg.

"You think so?" said Buchman. "Have you been following what is going on in Germany? The plan is to exterminate our people!" By now, Buchman's voice had risen, and the party came to a halt.

"Fun, people!" Carole Lombard insisted, parting the men. Dressed as a rootin', tootin' cowgirl, she drew two fake pistols out of their holsters and waved them around. "We are supposed to be having fun. You pardners best bust it up or this little lady will see you both pushin' up daisies." She said it with a smile and a drawl. There was a titter of appreciative laughter, but it could not dispel the tension in the air.

"It's hard to have fun while fellow Americans are on breadlines and can't find work." This was the quiet but mellifluous voice of Robert Riskin. "It's hard to have fun when the people of Spain are being murdered by a Fascist. It's hard to have fun when the Dust Bowl is sucking the life out of farmers. It's hard to have fun when migrants who organize are being beaten and called communists."

The party ended shortly after that. "He was brave to speak out," said Lu as she and Frank drove home.

"I voted for Alf Landon," Frank said. "He voted for Roosevelt. I don't believe in the New Deal and I don't believe in handouts. But I wonder sometimes why we have so much and why there is so much suffering, so much inequity."

They went back to their new home at 215 North Barrington Avenue. It was on a hill in Brentwood. Designed by celebrity architect Roland Coate, it had six bedrooms and sat on five acres. William Wellman, the director, and his wife, Dorothy, were neighbors and became good friends. Gary Cooper and his wife, Rocky, lived on an estate across the street. The Capras employed five servants and a gardener. Frank had helped plant some of the fruit trees and gardens that surrounded the house.

They kept the house in Malibu and went there on weekends in the summer. Frank loved being at the beach and sharing it with friends. He regularly taught their children to do headstands, as he himself often did on sets to break tension.

Another great pleasure was his rare books collection, which was valued at over $83,000. He had a special room built for the books. He loved to sit in the leather chair in the library and read. Holding the books was a tactile pleasure. They were his answer to a childhood in a home where the parents were illiterate and discouraged him from intellectual pursuits. He recalled himself as a young man sitting in the library at Anoakia, attempting to impart a love of learning to Lucky Baldwin's grandson. Frank had never forgotten Baldwin's sense of entitlement and lack of intellectual curiosity.

Frank also derived great pleasure from his beloved sons. Frank Jr. was a sturdy two-year-old whose resilience and tough spirit reminded Frank of his brother Tony. But for little baby John, everything seemed to be a struggle. "Some people are born with more to overcome than others," Frank often told himself. It made him ache with love for the little brown-haired infant whose eyes reminded him of Lu. He cherished both his boys, but the one who struggled had a special place in his heart.

Frank's fame was now such that there were constant requests for interviews and profiles. Collier's magazine did a lengthy article, mostly complimentary, but with allusions to his "gangster" anger when not winning at cards. Frank despised this insulting allusion to his heritage. It reminded him that prejudice was still alive no matter how successful he became. He resented it.

Robert Riskin, too, lived in a gorgeously appointed apartment in Hollywood with sumptuous furniture, Limoges china and closets full of custom-made clothing. Unlike Frank, who continued to have a contentious and strained relationship with his family, Riskin was close to his parents. They moved to Hollywood to be part of Riskin's life, and he supported them. Sarrida, on the other hand, came to the Brentwood house mainly to criticize and find fault with Lu and Frank for not introducing their children to enough religion.

For both men, the massive difference between the financial world of their upbringing and their current wealth affected them greatly. For Frank, there was a widening gap between the "little people" he portrayed on screen and the trappings of his own life.

As a wealthy man, he felt an obligation to pay attention to them and to dignify them.

Always on the search for new material, Frank encouraged Harry Cohn to purchase the rights to *Lost Horizon*, a best-selling novel by English writer James Hilton. The story of a man who finds eternal youth and peace in a place called Shangri-La appealed to a world on the verge of chaos. Frank began to contemplate a film based on the novel and felt that the only actor who could portray the lead character was Ronald Colman. Colman was unavailable for a year, so Frank put off the project and looked for something else while he waited.

He found "Opera Hat," a short story by Clarence Budington Kelland, self-described as "the best second-rate writer in America." Riskin was also attracted to the story and set about writing a screenplay, making several notable changes to the tale of a quiet, unassuming man from the small town of Mandrake Falls who suddenly inherits $20 million from a little-known uncle.

In Riskin's screenplay, Longfellow Deeds is humble but shrewd enough to see through people who want to dupe him. He questions the unscrupulous lawyer and the Algonquin-like crowd of writers who taunt and try to humiliate him. He suggests to an opera company seeking a large donation that they "try to run it more like a business." He allows himself to fall in love with a beautiful, scheming newspaperwoman.

In a key scene in the film, a farmer breaks into the palatial foyer of Deeds's home and makes an impassioned and heartbreaking speech condemning Deeds for living frivolously while people are starving, and for being selfish and petty while families have lost all they had. The speech changes Deeds, and he decides to give his money away as farms to those who qualify and will work. The final scene, in which a grasping relative accuses him of insanity, is full of insight, humor, and pathos. It brought into the American lexicon the word "pixilated," which two delightful characters use to describe the eccentric Longfellow Deeds.

Frank felt that the only actor who could play the passionate, thoughtful, humble, and honest Deeds was Gary Cooper. Columbia had to hold up production, costing them nearly $100,000, to wait for him. Carole Lombard was to have played the newspaperwoman who hoodwinks Deeds, then repents and falls in love with him. She backed out at the last minute.

Frank began shooting *Mr. Deeds Goes to Town* without having cast a leading lady. He happened to come upon rushes from another film that someone was watching in the Columbia screening room. He saw Jean Arthur, who was on contract at Columbia, and felt she had the right combination of strength, comedic timing, and authenticity to play the role of Babe Bennett.

Harry Cohn disagreed. Frank insisted. Arthur was a peculiar actress who suffered from nerves and anxiety. Before and after nearly every scene, she cried and vomited in her dressing room. She feared going in front of the camera, but once she was there, she was magnetic, surprising in her choices and, most important to Frank, utterly believable. Frank was sensitive and understanding with her quirks and willing to work around them, as he knew instinctively that audiences would believe her and love her. He was absolutely right.

Frank shot Riskin's script almost exactly as it had been written, with few changes. It was one of his favorites among all of Riskin's scripts, as it combined Frank's deep feeling for the downtrodden, his trademark takedowns of the wealthy and pretentious, and his sense of romanticism. The moment when Gary Cooper, as Longfellow Deeds, weeps behind a pillar after discovering Babe Bennett's duplicity, is masterful and touching. The moments in the film when Deeds demands that his manservant not get on his knees are humorous and moving.

Frank responded to the beauty and depth of the script by adding his own moments of inspiration throughout the film. He mixed sentimental moments, like the reading of Deeds's poem to Babe, with hilarious and human moments, such as when Deeds crashes into a trash can right after hearing her read the poem. The scene in which Jean Arthur as Babe Bennett and Gary Cooper as Longfellow Deeds pretend to play the drums and the tuba while falling in love is Frank Capra at his best: great emotion and great fun, abandon and freedom. Frank fell in love with the characters and the actors. He used Riskin's words and his own images to help the audience fall in love with them, too.

Mr. Deeds Goes to Town overtly referenced current politics. Despite their political differences, Capra and Riskin combined their creative strengths and humanity to make a film audiences in 1936 responded to with recognition and embrace. In Longfellow Deeds, they felt their voices were being heard; the description of what Deeds loved about Grant's Tomb was what they loved, too. Riskin put words to their emotions and Frank made them manifest.

Mr. Deeds Goes to Town allowed the two men—and a group of fellow artists they came to rely on, including Joe Walker, Ed Berends, and set designer Stephen Goosson—to work at the very best of their artistic potential. As an exploration of finding commonality and dignity, no scene can match the one in which Longfellow Deeds shares echoes with the servants in the house. It both exposes the hollowness of the marble foyer and brings warmth and humanity to it, and it encompasses one of the themes of the film: recognition of the dignity that resides in all of us.

As president of the Academy in 1937, Frank Capra was in a bind. Both the Writers Guild and Screen Actors Guild were encouraging their members to boycott the Oscars ceremony, due to their displeasure in negotiations with producers. As a last-minute act of desperation, Frank thought of the idea of honoring D. W. Griffith. He felt it might bring out both the curious and the respectful. He sent assistants in search of Griffith and he was found, eventually, in a nondescript bar in Kentucky. Frank was touched by this. The onetime greatest director in Hollywood was now reduced to drinking himself into a stupor, alone and all but forgotten. Frank was right; the presence of D. W. Griffith drew many who might have otherwise snubbed the event. Griffith was gracious and responsive, and the audience seemed to love the chance to recognize him. Nevertheless, the image of the lonely and forgotten man who had once been the toast of young Hollywood haunted Frank.

Mr. Deeds Goes to Town was nominated for Oscars in three categories: Best Director, Best Actor, and Best Screenplay. Frank believed that the script was the best Riskin had ever written and most certainly the best for that year. He was disappointed when Riskin didn't win and felt he had been robbed. When Frank's name was called as best director, host George Jessel couldn't resist making a joke about Frank's being the president of the Academy, insinuating that had something to do with his win.

The 1937 Academy Awards were further clouded for Frank by a brewing controversy over the film *Lost Horizon*. It would eventually forever alter his relationship with Harry Cohn. Worse, it would damage the one with Riskin.

Lost Horizon was a departure in almost every way for Frank Capra and Columbia Pictures. It cost six times more than *Mr. Deeds Goes to Town*: nearly $2 million. It was a morality tale that was set in many exotic locations in Shangri-La, not an office or urban street. It was a tale about a place where peace and immortality reign. It may have reflected Riskin's interest in Eastern philosophy as well as Frank's fascination with the confluence between religion, science, and philosophy.

Principal photography for *Lost Horizon* began March 23, 1936, and ended July 17, 1936. Cost overruns, highly unusual for Frank, were caused by difficulties in creating the locations and the wintry conditions of the Himalayas in the middle of the San Fernando Valley in summer. An elderly actor who had been found and cast in the role of the seer died suddenly days before the film was to begin shooting. When his housekeeper told him that he had won the role, he was so excited that he had a heart attack. Another elderly actor also died unexpectedly. Frank hired a younger actor, Sam Jaffe, to play the role.

For Frank, the making of *Lost Horizon* was an experience he cherished because of the challenges it presented. He was forced to come up with solutions both creative and scientific, and he relished every moment. For example, during a heat wave in Los Angeles, he filmed in an ice and storage warehouse to simulate the Himalayan weather.

Frank Capra's enjoyment was Harry Cohn's nightmare. The film went thirty-four days over schedule, the first cut was six hours long, and the amount of film was the most ever used on a single film up to that time. Economy of style and language seemed, for both Capra and Riskin, to have taken a back seat to experimentation and philosophy.

With help, Frank trimmed it to three and a half hours. Test audiences in Santa Barbara hooted with laughter in places that were supposed to be serious. Audiences leaving the theater proclaimed it a dud. Cohn was furious. The film had cost so much that the entire studio was in jeopardy. After the disastrous preview, Cohn insisted on editing the film himself. Screenwriter Sidney Buchman was called in to rewrite opening scenes, angering Riskin. The film broke boundaries and forged into new territory, but it did not please its producer, Harry Cohn.

Lost Horizon premiered on September 1, 1937, and received mixed reviews. Some thought it was a genius breakthrough for Frank Capra. Others, like Graham Greene, thought it was wildly excessive and too preachy.

Capra and Riskin, accompanied by Lu, who was pregnant

with her third child, traveled to London for the premiere of *Lost Horizon*. In a Europe that was on the verge of war, the message of hope and peace, of a world where one remained perpetually youthful, resonated deeply. Capra and Riskin left Lu in the care of friends in London and made a trip to the USSR. They were greeted as royalty by the Russian film community including the great Soviet director Sergei Eisenstein. The universal language of film was brought home to Frank as never before.

On returning to London, Capra happened to see a poster for a film titled *If You Could Only Cook* starring Jean Arthur. Underneath the title, in large letters, it said "A Frank Capra Production." It was from Columbia Pictures. Clearly Harry Cohn and Columbia were misusing his name to promote a film he had nothing to do with. Cohn and Frank were already at swords' points over the budget overruns for *Lost Horizon*. Frank was also in a salary dispute with Cohn. The obvious misuse of his name forced Frank to sue Cohn. The case was eventually dismissed on a technicality, but Frank refused to go back to Columbia.

Frank was out of Columbia and, for the first time in twenty years, out of work. He was bursting with notions for new films. He had perfected the art of working with actors, who adored him and who said their experiences working with him were the best in their careers. He had developed techniques, in concert with Joseph Walker, that revolutionized how scenes could be shot. He was at the top of his game. But he was vanquished for a time. It was as though Harry Cohn had decreed that Frank Capra didn't exist.

There was also a rift, discernible and real, between Frank Capra and Robert Riskin over how rewrites for *Lost Horizon* had been handled. Riskin wanted to go out on his own, away from the influence of Frank Capra.

Frank spent the fall of 1937 in a depressed state. The only thing that mitigated his negative mood was the birth of his daughter, Lulu, on September 16, 1937. She was a healthy baby girl whose presence added to the lively household. When Frank wasn't giving attention to his children, he put his excess energy into planting trees and gardening on his estate in Brentwood. He spent long hours at the beach house in Malibu with Lu and the children.

On a hot day in October, Johnny was crying and Frank Jr. was loudly singing a ditty over and over while throwing sand at his brother. Lu was reading a book and trying to ignore the childish behavior. Out of nowhere, Frank blew up at all of them, screaming at them to stop. The children were frozen and looked at their father in terror. Lu stared at Frank in disbelief. She had never heard her husband yell like that. Baby Lulu, who had been contentedly sleeping on a blanket, began to scream.

Frank was immediately ashamed. It brought back memories of daily fights when he was growing up. The last thing he wanted to do was to behave like this with his own precious family. They meant everything to him. He apologized to them, something neither of his parents had ever done. Lu and a sad-faced Frank Jr. accepted his apology. But Frank understood that the incident would not be forgotten.

Frank continued to refuse to return to Columbia and Harry

Cohn. One day in November, 1937, the Capras' housekeeper came to Frank, who was sitting in his library at their home on Barrington. "There is a Mr. Cohn to see you," she said.

Frank was stunned. Harry Cohn, standing in the foyer of his house? It was unexpected and completely out of character. Frank walked out and there he was. Although it was a hot day, Cohn was wearing a wool topcoat and fedora. He was not a tall man, but his presence and solid build made it seem as though he filled the whole space.

"Harry, it's good to see you—" Frank began.

"Damn it, let's get down to brass tacks," Harry interrupted. "I have beaten that son of a bitch L. B. Mayer to the rights for that damn play everybody seems to love. I don't get it, but I don't care. Who wants to see a bunch of nuts in a nuthouse? But I bought the rights for *You Can't Take It With You* right out from under that SOB's nose. It cost me $200,000. And it's yours if you want to direct it. I drove all the way down Wilshire and out to this godforsaken Brentwood to say this. Now I'm getting back in my car and you can call me."

With that, he turned on his heel and prepared to leave.

"Harry," said Frank, "stay for a drink."

He did.

People try, but they don't ever really forget hurts and slights, particularly people with egos like Harry Cohn and Frank Capra. They compartmentalize them. Robert Riskin felt, rightfully so, that he needed to write and produce his own films. They all decided to put the past on the shelf and work together again, however. *You Can't Take It With You* was a new start for Frank back at Columbia. The people he had worked with for a decade and whose respect he had earned welcomed him back with open arms. But the rift between Cohn and Capra, despite the string of hits they had created together, made Cohn more determined than ever to remain in charge and to show that he was in charge. New York kept reminding him of the excesses of *Lost Horizon*; it had not been a financial success. This was the ultimate sin. Robert Riskin, though still a friend, was actively pursuing a plan to strike out on his own at another studio.

Frank Capra, the director beloved by his cast and crews, lauded by the Academy and arguably the person whose work, along with that of Robert Riskin, had put Columbia Pictures on the map, returned to Columbia. Everyone from the gate guard to Cohn appeared relieved and happy to have him back. As the world drew nearer to tragedy on an inconceivable scale, Frank's next three films enlarged the panorama of American life. They veered from an eccentric family to an idealistic politician battling greed and corruption. All captured, in some way, truths about the American spirit as well as reflections about the inner life of their maker.

As a measure of the respect with which his peers in the industry held him, Frank was elected president of the Screen Directors Guild, a position he held from 1938 to 1941. The four years between 1937 and the start of World War II would bring Frank Capra, the ebullient, warm man of art and science, great triumph and unimagined tragedy.

Chapter Nine

THE EMBRACE OF RESILIENCY

The shouting could be heard all the way down in the court-yard with the nonworking fountain that was used as an ashtray. Harry Cohn and his brother Jack were arguing about losses from *Lost Horizon*. Then Jack went on a tirade about Harry spending $200,000 on the rights to *You Can't Take It With You*.

It was nothing unusual. Jack Cohn was in town from New York, bringing gloom and doom from the East Coast. He was berating Harry. The screaming and abuse filled the hallway as Frank walked toward Harry's office. The secretaries in the outer office were used to the yelling and barely took note. Harry's door was ajar and Frank stepped inside. The two men were so incensed they didn't notice Frank's presence. They did stop, however, for a high-pitched tinkling sound that came from an ice cream truck that had pulled up on Gower. Without skipping a beat, Harry said, "Vanilla or chocolate?"

Jack Cohn answered, "Chocolate."

Harry said, "Well, gimme your nickel." His brother flipped him a coin. Harry grabbed a nickel out of his own pocket, leaned his head out the open window, threw down the money and yelled an order to the ice cream man. In a moment, two ice cream bars came sailing through the window. Cohn threw one to his brother. They resumed screaming precisely where they had left off.

Frank had seen George S. Kaufman and Moss Hart's *You Can't Take It With You* on Broadway. The play about the ups and downs of the eccentric Vanderhof family, with its emphasis on art over money, had been the object of a bidding war between Louis B. Mayer and Harry Cohn. Cohn spent $200,000 on the rights for the play, a sum that made his brother apoplectic. But to whisk it away from under Mayer's nose, Cohn would have spent almost any amount. He gleefully offered it to Frank to direct as an enticement to come back to Columbia. Frank was happy to oblige.

Whereas Frank had created an external Shangri-La for *Lost Horizon*, *You Can't Take It With You* reflects a kind of internal Shangri-La. The Vanderhof home is a place of acceptance, freedom, and honoring the dignity of each individual. The kindness and humanity exemplified by Grandpa Vanderhof grants everyone who enters the home, even the IRS man, a sense of automatic grace, whether they have earned it or not. The entire family is spending their lives doing what they love. Grandpa's speech about "isms" reflects a humorous take on blind obedience to a cause. The quirky and charming Vanderhof family serves as a way for the creators to ask a profound question about the kinds of choices every human being makes about how to spend the time we are given.

With Riskin on board to do the adaptation, Frank was able to attract a perfect cast, including one of his all-time favorite actors, Lionel Barrymore. Barrymore was suffering from severe arthritis, but a line in the screenplay explained his cane and "broken foot" by saying that he had done it sliding down a banister. Frank Capra noticed a young actor who had a small part in the MGM film *Navy Blue and Gold*. He thought that the actor's gangly charm and authenticity would work well for the role of Tony Kirby. The actor was Jimmy Stewart, and his role in the film would catapult him to fame.

The rest of the cast was rounded out by what had become Capra's "stock company" of character actors. These were actors he had used frequently in his previous films and who loved working with him. Edward Arnold often played the "heavy," the gruff businessman. Ann Doran, Donald Meek, and Spring Byington were actors Frank respected and admired, and he used them whenever he could. To a person, they found Frank's methods of working with actors creative, inspiring, and respectful.

Before shooting a scene, Frank sat in a circle with the actors and read through it, emphasizing that they were not to "act." He just wanted them to read and be themselves doing the role. He had specific ideas about what he wanted to get out of scenes and what part each scene had in the overall story. But he often asked actors what they thought they might do in a given situation. He asked for creative solutions from actors and crew. He was always willing to listen and to use their suggestions if he thought they were good. He loved what the actors brought to their work and allowed them to create and use bits of their own.

Frank was able to create a joyful and inclusive atmosphere on his sets. This energy and spirit found its way into every frame of *You Can't Take It With You*. Frank became more fascinated than ever with the use of reaction shots: silent, private moments that spoke volumes about the internal thoughts and feelings of a character at a particular time. These moments brought the audience inside the characters and made them feel as though they were an integral part of the experience. In Frank's mind, they absolutely were.

Frank Capra was now forty years old. In the time between *Lost Horizon* and *You Can't Take It With You*, when he was absent from Columbia, he had a chance to bond with his family, to finish the house in Brentwood, and to follow in his father's footsteps by planting a small orchard on his property. He even started music lessons with his friend, the composer Dmitri Tiomkin. He missed making films, and the time away give him a chance to understand how the addictive quality of filmmaking—the community of it, the total absorption of it, the daily pressure of making thousands of decisions—was in his soul.

The physical distance from Castelar Street, where he first lived as a boy, to Barrington Avenue was less than fourteen miles, but it was a lifetime of experience. That boy was now a man whose image graced one of the most iconic magazines published in America. On August 8, 1938, Frank Capra's picture was on the cover of *Time* magazine. The photograph shows a man dressed in a sweater and corduroys, as if for work, with a rakish, confident smile. He is holding a pipe. He looks like someone you might enjoy having for a neighbor; someone whose advice you might seek, or who would be fun to sit next to at a dinner party. The profile mentioned his battles with Harry Cohn and Columbia and described him as an energetic, charming, unpretentious, and intelligent man. It also detailed his love for his wife, Lu, and his family.

Harry Cohn and Columbia were pleased with *You Can't Take It With You*. So pleased they decided to go all-out for a press preview on August 23, 1938. Several thousand journalists, publicists, and fans were invited to a sit-down lunch, a free bar, and a viewing of the film. The largest soundstage at Columbia was decorated for the occasion. Flags and banners hung from light poles for blocks around.

As president of the Academy and the Directors Guild, Frank had been involved in intense negotiations with the National Labor Relations Board. On August 22, the night prior to the preview, he had s six-hour meeting. An event of utmost importance in his life was scheduled for the morning of August 23. Johnny Capra, now almost three and a half years old, would undergo a tonsillectomy. Doctors thought it might improve his tendency to get colds and also help with his speech. Although slow to speak, as of late, he had been naming things and using words correctly.

Lu wept in gratitude when the doctors described what the surgery might do for Johnny, and Frank saw the depth of her concern. She seemed lighter and happier, and Frank understood she had kept her worries to herself in order not to burden him. It made him love her all the more.

On August 23, the Capras piled into the car for the ride to

Children's Hospital on Vermont and Sunset. Frank, Lu, Johnny, and Johnny's nurse were vastly amused as the boy pointed out objects, screaming with delight when they nodded approval. It was a joyous ride. They worried to see him wheeled away by white-coated nurses but breathed sighs of relief in an hour, when Johnny's doctor came into the waiting room with a broad smile. "Smooth as silk. It's all fine, and he'll be asleep for a few hours."

Lu urged Frank to go to the press preview. "He'll be asleep. You'll be back by the time he wakes up. Go, darling. Enjoy. He'll never know you were gone."

Frank looked through the tiny window of the recovery room. Joseph Walker couldn't have framed it better. There was his son, sleeping on his stomach with those tufts of brown soft baby hair.

Frank drove down Sunset Boulevard toward Columbia. He had walked down Sunset so many times. When he lived in the apartment in Hollywood with Helen and had no car. When he went with Mack Sennett to the Musso and Frank Grill. When he made his way to Columbia for the first time. The street had changed, grown more sophisticated.

Frank chuckled to himself, wondering if he, too, had changed. Despite the awards and the trappings of wealth, he still felt like the same boy who had sold newspapers where Sunset became Figueroa. There was one difference: he had a family that he loved and that loved him. He was no longer lonely. They filled his heart and soul and gave meaning to his life.

Frank turned left from Sunset onto Bronson. The street was filled with fluttering banners proclaiming the premiere of *You*

Can't Take It With You. It was a gay scene; crowds surged toward the gate. A band ws playing "I've Got a Pocket Full of Dreams." Frank whistled along and the police, recognizing him, made way for his car.

As he approached the studio gate, his old friend Mac the guard, who Frank had met on his first day at Columbia, ran out to the car. He put his face into the window. It was ashen. "You need to go back to the hospital. Right now. Your wife just called."

Frank drove like a maniac. He pulled up in front of the hospital and ran to the third floor. Three figures stood at the end of the hallway: Lu, Johnny's nurse, and the doctor. A shaft of sunlight came through the window and obscured their faces. But he could hear the sobbing. He could hear his wife's unearthly wailing.

Frank reached Lu and enveloped her in his arms. Her face was wet with tears. She whispered into his ear, "He's gone. Our baby is gone. It was a blood clot, Frank." She was shaking uncontrollably. "There was nothing anyone could do. Oh, Frank, what will we do without our Johnny?"

After that, Frank Capra was never the same. For the rest of his life, his natural ebullience was tinged with grief and pain that subsided at times but never went away. When Frank's father, Turridu, died his terrible death in the pump house, Frank lost part of his history, part of the context for his life. His youth and drive allowed him to reimagine a new life, to remake his history. In losing his son, he lost a part of himself, a part of his hope, a part of his confidence that things would turn out for the best.

From then on, Frank looked over his shoulder, trying to protect himself from the inevitable tragedies of life. He became more determined than ever to control and to be credited for what he created. If life was unpredictable and often cruel and unfair, Frank was going to make certain that he would be in charge of the things he could control.

The grief that Frank carried within him weighed him down so much that at times, during the ensuing weeks, he could barely function. He remained a passionate, unpretentious storyteller and chronicler of the human condition. But the man the crew had come to know, especially Joe Walker and Ed Berends, who had worked with him for more than a decade day in and day out, had changed. At forty years old, Frank had experienced the pinnacle of success and the depths of tragic loss.

In 1939, Frank Capra would receive his third Oscar for directing for *You Can't Take It With You*. The film also won Best Picture. But the grief from Johnny's death hung on him and would not go away.

Frank's next film, *Mr. Smith Goes to Washington*, would receive a mixed reaction from the American public and especially American politicians. Sidney Buchman, an urbane and witty writer from the Columbia stable, wrote the screenplay. Robert Riskin, determined to free himself from the shadow of Frank Capra, worked on producing his own film.

Mr. Smith Goes to Washington is a tale about an everyman, played by Jimmy Stewart, who becomes a senator and stands up to the greed and duplicitousness in Washington. He is set up by a cynical, hard-driven female journalist who ultimately falls in love with him for his ethics and strength of character. Stewart knew this was an important role and was forever grateful to Frank for casting him. Stewart was so terrified that something would happen to him during the filming that he reportedly drove to the studio each day, never going over ten miles an hour. Frank was overjoyed to be able to cast his old friend Harry Carey in the role of the president of the senate. Carey had predicted Frank's career in film, and he had been right.

The stage was set for a major premiere in Washington, DC, on October 17, 1939. Washington was thrilled to have a famous Hollywood director in its midst. However, the reception for the film was decidedly mixed. The depiction of greed and venality among the senators was said by some to be unpatriotic, especially as the nation began to prepare for what some saw as the inevitable buildup to war. Some directly accused Buchman of being a Communist sympathizer. Frank vehemently defended his film and Buchman, pointing out that the message of his film was the preciousness of freedom and the fundamental importance of acknowledging it. Harry Cohn eventually stood by the film, although there were many tense arguments prior to its release to the general public. Ambassador Joseph P. Kennedy opposed it and wrote a letter saying so.

Mr. Smith Goes to Washington was a huge hit with the general public. Jimmy Stewart was catapulted to stardom and a place among the pantheon of Hollywood greats. Frank Capra, the Italian immigrant, had used his fundamental right as an American citizen to criticize his country, and in so doing had emphasized his pride in and love for his country. He and many others felt that the picture was the epitome of patriotism in showing, in the character of Mr. Smith, what the word *democracy* really means.

Later that month, Frank took a final walk around the Columbia lot. His picture deal with Cohn was completed. It was time to move on. He noted the same rickety stairs he had walked up twelve years before and heard the same shouting secretaries.

Harry Cohn still ruled the lot with an iron hand. He had given Frank a certain kind of freedom as a producer, and Frank had repaid him with a shelf full of Oscars, representing respect from the Hollywood community and fans worldwide. He had become arguably one of the most revered directors in Hollywood, having won three Oscars for Best Director. He had served as president of the Academy and was president of the Screen Directors Guild. Frank had raised the level of storytelling, and working as a team, albeit a contentious, fractious one, he and Cohn had served each other well.

Capra said good-bye to everyone from the executive secretaries to the lowliest grips. They were all sad to see him go. They had come to know him as a person unconcerned with status, only concerned with telling the story well. They had known him to listen carefully and to take suggestions from just about anyone. The idea mattered most. If it struck him as worthwhile, he would find a way to make it work. That was who Frank Capra was. This was a stark contrast to their boss, Harry Cohn.

Frank walked to his office. The late afternoon Santa Ana winds blew hot and dusty. It was time to leave and to strike out on his own, to work somewhere else. To be in charge. Truly in charge. He waited for a visit, a good-bye toast, from Harry Cohn or any of his associates from across the lot. They never came. Frank closed his office door and made sure the light was off. It was a habit after twelve years of working for Harry Cohn.

Frank's working relationship with Harry Cohn and Columbia Pictures from 1927 to 1939 was a unique and productive one. It had made him a wealthy man. In 1939, he fulfilled a lifelong dream of his father's by purchasing a ranch in Fallbrook, a small California farming community 100 miles from Los Angeles. A historic ranch house with a white clapboard porch, designed by the architect Stanford White, graced the 536-acre property, which featured groves of olive and citrus trees and an olive press. Frank's father-in-law managed the ranch, and for a time it made and sold Fallbrook Olive Oil, "produced by Frank Capra."

Twenty years after Turridu's death, his son had attained something he had never had in life: land of his own and a place of peace and beauty. The purchase of the property may have also symbolized Frank's own need to occasionally escape the continuing tensions of life on the high wire of the entertainment business, and his desire to keep making personally meaningful work with mass appeal.

In October 1939, Frank realized a professional dream by starting his own production company with Robert Riskin as a partner. Riskin had left Columbia to work for producer Sam Goldwyn but found that freedom, under the thumb of Sam Goldwyn, was not free. He was eager to start anew without the force of either Harry Cohn or Sam Goldwyn.

Running a company meant that Frank needed to shed some of his outside jobs, and he resigned as president of the Academy. Director Victor Fleming's *Gone with the Wind* swept the 1940 Oscars.

With his cameraman Joseph Walker and another friend, Frank pursued a research and development company. They developed the zoom lens, a selenium grid for military use against the blinding light of flares dropped from bombers, and wind cups for landing aircraft to eliminate burning rubber. They experimented with cryptography (code) machines, also for military use. Even while directing, producing, and serving the Academy and his union as well as raising a family, Frank had never forgotten his love of science and invention.

Frank Capra Productions' first and only film was *Meet John Doe*. Riskin and Frank abandoned their usual hero, the Candide-like innocent besieged by greed and venality. Instead, they began the film with a hero who is devoid at first of moral purpose but finds it, only to be disbelieved. They cast favorites Gary Cooper and Barbara Stanwyck in the two leads but couldn't decide on an ending. They called in Jules Furthman, a "story doctor" renowned for his ability to remember stories and plots. He was no help. They finally decided to let the crowd of John Does dissuade John Doe the character from jumping to his suicide. Critics favored the film; audiences did not.

On February 12, 1941, Lu Capra gave birth to son Tom. He joined big brother Frank, who was now seven, and sister Lu, who was four. Sarrida Capra made fewer and fewer visits to their home in Brentwood. She remained disapproving of what she considered the lack of religion in their lives. Frank never gave up trying to please her, and he never forgot the sacrifice and backbreaking work she had undertaken, when he was a boy, to keep bread on the table and a roof over their heads.

The joyous occasion of Tom's birth was clouded by a downturn in Sarrida's health. As Tom was born, Sarrida was being wheeled into surgery at Cedars-Sinai Hospital. Frank was there as her leg, which had been rendered useless by thrombosis, was amputated. She was cheered, temporarily, by the news of her new grandson. A week later, pneumonia set in. Surrounded by family, she passed away quietly on February 20, 1941.

Frank held Sarrida's tough love in the highest regard. Like many immigrants of her generation, her resilience and grit had allowed her children to not only survive in America but to accomplish things she never could have dreamed. Frank forever remembered and cherished her willingness to sacrifice to make a better life for her children. She was not a woman who had time for sentiment or constant expressions of love. She showed her love by conceiving of a new life, a different life, in America. She believed that nothing ever came to anyone by chance. Rewards were the result of hard work and sacrifice. Frank recognized and was grateful for her indomitable spirit.

Frank and Riskin abandoned their new company when they realized that taxes would take nearly ninety percent of the profit they made from *Meet John Doe*. Several studios came through with offers to hire Frank Capra. The events of December 7, 1941, would overshadow everything. Japan's attack on Pearl Harbor would assure American's entrance into World War II.

Frank set his sights on Washington, DC. He wanted to join the war effort—not teaching math to ballistics experts, as he did during World War I, but somewhere he could use every fiber of his creativity and intelligence.

A deeply troubling episode with his sister Anne, who had never become a U.S. citizen and was for a while declared an enemy alien, shook Frank to the core and reminded him that no matter what he or his family did, the Capras had begun their lives as immigrants. They were from a foreign country, a country that was now an enemy of America.

The war was changing attitudes toward foreign-born people, allowing prejudice to surface. This would continue and make itself felt for years to come. Despite the films Frank had made proclaiming and giving voice to the American spirit, and the many ways his accomplishments had been celebrated, it was still possible for his own sister to be threatened and ostracized.

The tension inherent in this resonated deep within Frank Capra. He had straddled the line between his Republican beliefs and anti-union sentiments and his leadership of the Academy and the Screen Directors Guild. He was an ardent believer in the American dream and also felt free to criticize his country as part of his citizenship. Most of all, he was eager to keep proving his love for America.

Before he left for Washington and military service, Frank had to face the fact that he had mortgaged his home and future to finance *Meet John Doe*. He still had a family to support. Despite offers from Twentieth Century-Fox for his services, including one his agent said he would never get again, Frank turned away from Hollywood to serve his country.

He made one last film before joining up. He had seen *Arsenic and Old Lace*, written by Howard Lindsay and Russell Crouse, on Broadway, and knew it could be turned into a screenplay. He proposed a four-week shooting schedule, with Cary Grant to star, and had a simple set built.

During the third week of the shoot, two officers from the Signal Corps appeared on the set to swear Frank Capra in as a major in the US Army. Although it was unclear exactly what his work would entail, he knew it would involve filmmaking on some level. He undertook his physicals and army paperwork while completing the editing of *Arsenic and Old Lace*. Lu helped him pack uniforms into a duffel bag and drove him to the station with a final admonishment, "Don't try to direct the army, darling."

Frank realized he was leaving behind lucrative offers and a career that was at its zenith. He knew that, as a man at the pinnacle of his success and reputation, the offers might evaporate once he returned to Hollywood. In fact, it was almost assured. But he was deeply patriotic. He had also grown weary of the opulence of his life and the chasm between the little people he championed onscreen and his own lifestyle. He found the "fast set" in Hollywood as inane, at times, as the dinner table at the Baldwins so many years before. He needed a challenge—a different kind of challenge.

After being followed by journalists, sought after at lavish

Hollywood premieres, and hounded by gossip columnists, Frank Capra left on a train with no fanfare, a big bag full of uniforms, and only Lu to say good-bye. He had kissed his children good-bye at home. He carried his own bag, hoisted it into the train car, and slept, along with hundreds of soldiers, not in a fancy Pullman car but in his seat, all the way from L.A. to Washington, DC.

Involvement in the war effort removed any sense of ego, self-promotion, or concern for self. Frank plunged eagerly into the world and the work. For him, it was both a respite from the kinds of pressures he had been handling for so many years and a way to do something for his country. In joining the war effort, Frank mirrored William Wyler, John Ford, and George Stevens, all mid-career directors with families and decades in the entertainment business.

He brought a multiplicity of talents to the table: his ability to work fast; his desire to work for a cause greater than himself; his native ingenuity; engineering skills, people skills, organizational and leadership skills developed over nearly twenty years of working in production; his ability to see the big picture as well as break things down into steps; the stamina he had developed over many years of fourteen-hour days. More than anything, giving of himself to the war effort allowed Frank to interact with a variety of Americans who embodied the best the country had to give. It reinforced his belief in the country he loved.

Like others from Hollywood who served, he had no idea exactly how long he would be away. At the moment, he didn't care. He could not have known that it would be years, not months, and that his service and the experience would change him forever. The war would end eventually. But its effects would remain with those who served until the end of their days. Frank could not have foreseen any of this when his train pulled into Washington, DC, in February 1942.

Frank was used to being wined and dined as a celebrity. He arrived in a Washington that was overflowing with soldiers looking for accommodation. Every hotel, every restaurant, every street was teeming with activity. There was no one to carry his bags and no one to ask him to dinner.

He was assigned at first to the Signal Corps, which had sumptuous offices, and where Darryl F. Zanuck, on leave from Twentieth Century-Fox, was head administrator. He was soon reassigned to the "morale branch." Its command consisted of a tall, elderly brigadier general named Frederick Osborn and a compact young man, a graduate of West Point, named Lyman Munson. Munson was full of wit and ironic humor, and Frank immediately recognized in him someone of substance and depth. They would become great friends.

Over lunch on Frank's first day, Munson explained that he had been hand-picked by General George C. Marshall. The Signal Corps jealously guarded its right to be the only part of the army to deal with film. But their products were boring and desultory. The fighting men needed something to inspire them, to give them a reason why they were fighting. General Marshall felt that if Frank Capra could buck the establishment in Holly-wood, as he had done coming from Poverty Row, he could do the same in the army.

Frank was ready for the challenge. He came to understand that part of his assignment would be to find a way around the Signal Corps and produce his own riveting films for the morale branch.

General George C. Marshall was a graduate of the Virginia Military Institute (VMI) and had served under General John J. Pershing in World War I. General Marshall was now the US Army's Chief of Staff. Inheriting a largely outmoded and poorly equipped army, he was in charge of preparing and organizing the largest military expansion in United States history while coordinating a massive training effort as well as modernization. Faced with turning an army of 180,000 soldiers into a fighting force eight million strong, General Marshall drew on every technique he had learned in his years in the army, and most particularly on those he had learned working with young men at the army war college. Well aware of the power of film, he wisely chose Frank Capra to produce films that would create understanding and inspiration.

During their first meeting, General Marshall impressed Frank Capra deeply with his focus, his understanding of the enormity of the task ahead, and the specific need to turn young men, some of whom had never held guns, into a fighting force. Marshall had an intrinsic belief in the potential of the American solider, imbued with a love of country, to defend it if they knew why.

Frank Capra understood that he was being asked to make a certain kind of film, a kind he had never made before. General Marshall countered that many men fighting had never seen a gun or an ocean or been on a plane before. They had never been shot at before. In other words, everyone was being asked to do things they had never done before. Frank needed no more convincing. This was a struggle for men's minds. The garden-variety training films put out by the Signal Corps wouldn't do.

After viewing the visual blunderbuss of German film director Leni Riefenstahl's *Triumph of the Will*, Frank pondered how he could create an equally powerful response. He made friends with a rousing group that included Lyman Munson and his wife, both the children of West Pointers, and their friend Eric Knight, a noted British author. Together they explored ways to make films that would empower the American soldier. Frank came up with the idea of using the enemy's own films to explore their evil. He used $3,000 of his own money to buy newsreel footage from Europe's Pathé News. He began gathering newsreel footage whenever he could, often just a few steps ahead of the Signal Corps.

Frank Capra eventually made seven *Why We Fight* films, largely using footage from German, Japanese, and Russian newsreels. Anatole Litvak, William Shirer, Paul Horgan, James Hilton, and Leonard Spiegelglass were just some of the directors, journalists, and writers who worked with him on the films.

Frank's room 308 at the Carlton Hotel in Washington, DC, became a meeting place, a club room of sorts, for some of the greatest minds of the time. They socialized, plotted ideas, and shared their hopes and dreams. Composer Kurt Weill and playwrights Marc Connelly and Charles MacArthur were just a few of the luminaries who made their way to room 308. It was a tiny room, but the circumstance of the war made it a hotbed of creativity.

Frank organized the information-gathering, translating, editing, writing, and producing of the films. He did so with ingenuity, respect for his peers, and an attitude of completing what he started, no matter the obstacles. He never forgot General Marshall's words, or the men and women who were in harm's way, or about to be. He worked tirelessly.

General Marshall was enormously grateful for Frank's work and the films he produced. The two men became friends during the war years, enjoying dinners together, talking about anything but the war. They shared a vital interest in horticulture and a mutual interest in each other's lives, Frank in Marshall's military career and Marshall in Frank's Hollywood experience. Both had an abiding interest in discussing what causes people to excel, to push past what they thought they could do.

Frank had occasion to meet and show a film for President Franklin D. Roosevelt himself. Though he was not a fan of FDR, he couldn't help but be impressed by his charm, deep intelligence, and presence. He traveled to England to meet and photograph Winston Churchill and saw the effects of the bombing raids on the populace, experiencing one raid himself. Frank was deeply affected by the pain, fear, and terror that he saw on the faces of the British people, as well as their determination and resilience.

Frank Capra was discharged on was June 14, 1945. As he was packing up his office, he was summoned to General Marshall. All the officers with whom he had served were gathered. General Marshall presented him with the Distinguished Service Medal, the highest honor that can be bestowed on a noncombatant. It was a highlight of Frank's life. The immigrant boy who had sold newspapers to wealthy and powerful citizens, looking up at them with awe, was now being honored by one of America's greatest military leaders.

Surely Frank Capra was now inextricably American in every way. He had proven it with his artistry, his own leadership, and his relentless pursuit of excellence with the documentaries he created during World War II. The political fallout from the McCarthy Era and the Cold War would later prove challenging for him. But for now, Frank embodied everything that his classmate from Manual Arts, General James Doolittle, meant when he said, "I am a lifelong admirer of Frank Capra."

Chapter Ten

THE EMBRACE OF RESURRECTION

Frank Capra was doing his best to tell the story. "There is a man, a man who has taken over running a Savings and Loan in a small town, Bedford Falls, against his will, and his dreams of travel and adventure and making something of himself have been squashed, see, by circumstances beyond his control, and so he decides to commit suicide."

He took a breath and looked around at the people who were listening to him: the actor Jimmy Stewart; Lew Wasserman, Jimmy's agent; and Sam Briskin, former assistant to Harry Cohn, now a producer and Frank's partner in the newly formed Liberty Films. They all stared at him wide-eyed, waiting, Frank feared, for the story to pick up. He tried to oblige.

"An angel comes, you see . . . and . . . and shows him what it would have been like if he'd never existed . . . shows him that his life was worth something." He stopped short to see if they seemed convinced of anything. They did not.

Ever gracious, Jimmy Stewart stepped in. "So . . . suicide

and . . . hmmn . . . an angel. Well, if it's good enough for Frank Capra, it's good enough for me. I'm in."

Frank knew that Stewart, always loyal, was agreeing to do it out of gratitude for all Frank had done for him. He certainly wasn't sold on the story. Frank also knew that to do the film, the first order of business was getting Jimmy Stewart to star. If this didn't happen, nothing else would.

This was the first time Frank had seen Stewart since before the war. There was a haunted look about him now. After five years in the air force flying twenty-plus missions over Germany in a B-24 Liberator, seeing countless men never return and wondering if he would be next, Stewart was forever changed.

Frank had served his country by making films to inspire and motivate enlisted men. But he never faced fire. He didn't face losing men he had worked with and come to respect and admire. He had done whatever was asked of him. But as he studied Stewart, seated with the others in a fancy office high above Wilshire Boulevard, Frank could see that five years of fear, uncertainty, and the responsibility of having to lead men by reining in emotion, and attending to the job while flying into the darkness over Germany, had taken their toll.

Jimmy Stewart had experienced war in a very different way than Frank Capra had. It was visible in the shadows under his eyes and the hollows in his cheeks. The smooth-faced, gangly Indiana boy from *You Can't Take It With You* was gone. In its place was a man who had faced unspeakable horror and stuffed it inside. It had nowhere to go, so it lived under his skin, right near the surface, ready to explode.

Wasserman and Briskin left. They knew Capra and Stewart would overcome any objections they had to the project, so they admitted defeat.

Stewart took a deep breath. "Frank, I don't know if I can act anymore. I'm grateful to you. You know I am. But I'm thinking of giving it up. Just moving back to Indiana and working with my father. He wants me to."

Stewart stared at the floor, and Frank noticed that his hands were shaking. Frank was dumbfounded. But he knew there was no actor better for the part of George Bailey, a man on the edge, a man seriously contemplating ending his own life. Frank pondered for a moment whether it was actually good for a man in Stewart's obviously unsteady mental state to tackle such a role. Then he considered that it might help him heal.

"This is not really a film about savings and loans and so forth," Frank said. "It's about a man's battle with himself. A battle with self-doubt, with fear, the kind that overtakes everything. With the loneliness and isolation of what it sometimes means to be alive. It's about what is really worth living for, not dying for. What makes life worth all the pain and suffering? What makes it worth going on another day? How do we exorcise the demons? I'm scared, too. I haven't directed anything but documentaries in four years."

Frank stopped. He realized he was talking about himself. Then he shrugged and said, "Oh, hell, I'm talking in riddles. I sound ridiculous. Let's just have some fun, okay? Let's have some fun with this."

Jimmy Stewart stood up to his full height. He towered over

Frank. "If you want the truth," he said, "I've been thinking about that every day for the last five years. You know I'll work hard for you, Frank. I'd do anything for you. But one thing. No mention, ever, of my war record. Nothing. Do you hear me?"

His voice began to rise. "I am not a hero. Do you hear me? I am not! The ones who didn't come back are the heroes. I'm not using this, these soldiers, what they did, what they suffered, what *they* suffered, not *me*, to sell movies, do you understand? To make money for people, to sell tickets and popcorn . . . . If I see one word about my war record anywhere, ever, I'm out. Also, I can't drive. No scenes with driving. If there is any driving, you'll have to make it a taxi."

By now, Stewart was sweating profusely. He collapsed back into his chair.

"Can I give you a ride home, Jimmy? Where are you staying?" asked Frank.

Stewart laughed and the tension was broken. "I am living in the playhouse Hank Fonda built for his kids, Jane and Peter," he said. "It's quiet back there in their yard, and safe, and I can think. Hank and I sit and make model airplanes. It kind of takes the edge off, you know?"

"I know," said Frank. "Oh, how I know. I do the same thing at my cabin in the High Sierra. Just put out my fishing line and think."

Like every person who served in the war, Frank came back a changed person to a changed world. Like every parent who had served throughout the war, he returned to children who had grown older. Frank Jr. was verging on adolescence. Capra's complete and total focus on his army service had meant there was little to spare for his family.

He left behind a thriving career and a town that was clamoring for him after the momentum of nearly twenty years. Now the momentum had been halted. He left a Hollywood transfixed by comedies and yearning for hope for the depressed, downtrodden individual. He left a world that had a seen a zenith of attendance at films, and an audience whose joys and triumphs he seemed to understand and mirror onscreen. Now those audiences had undergone the trauma of grief and loss. They had witnessed the atrocities of war on those same screens. They had seen the battles, the fierce and unending blood and gore, the shock and horror of the concentration camps. They were different people. America was a different country.

Frank returned home in May of 1945, after receiving the Distinguished Service Medal, to a Hollywood that was already being challenged by the stirrings of McCarthyism. The House Un-American Activities Committee (HUAC) had begun its relentless investigations of people they deemed radicals. Nearly sixty per cent of those investigated were writers. Many were writers with whom Frank Capra had worked and with whom he had close personal and professional relationships. Ultimately, HUAC claimed that Communist writers, or writers who sympathized with Communists, had been placing coercive and negative messages, sometimes subliminal, into Hollywood films for years.

The anti-Communist hysteria that boiled up after World War II had been simmering since the early 1930s, with committees established by Senator Martin Dies Jr. of Texas and Senator Jack B. Tenney of California. HUAC claimed that any film they deemed critical of American finance, politics, or foreign policy was suspect. When writers were subpoenaed to appear before the committee, admit their association with communism and name names, their natural impulse was to fight back. Within the Screen Directors Guild, there was an immediate schism between those who wanted to demand a "loyalty oath," declaring the signer had no association either past or present with the Communist Party, and those who found this demand fundamentally abhorrent and un-American. The first writers called before HUAC were shouted down when they attempted to read a statement of protest.

In this atmosphere of fear, tension, anger, and paranoia, it was impossible to stay neutral. Fame and celebrity were no protection and often made things more difficult. Lives, livelihoods, friendships, and artistic partnerships were all at stake. The HUAC committee combed through past films, interviews, profiles, photographs, personal and professional relationships of any kind, and any other evidence they could find to prove Communist association. They solicited informers and planted them within the Hollywood community.

After fighting a war in Europe, many of the directors, writers, and actors who had served their country valiantly now returned to fight a different kind of war within the industry. It had a devastating effect on the lives of many people. Frank Capra was one of them.

As a child, he was an outsider in America, fighting for an education. As a young man, he got to know his fellow Americans through his years of wandering in California, Oregon, Utah, and Arizona selling Elbert Hubbard's books. He sat in people's kitchens, saw their farms, and talked to them. He spent twenty years reflecting their unique individuality onscreen. Then he served his country for four years, using every skill he had to inspire those who were fighting to protect democracy and remind them why they were doing so.

Now he discovered that the FBI had created a file on him as early as 1932. For a man who was a proud American and who considered himself to be a dedicated patriot, this knowledge was deeply disturbing. It affected nearly every choice he was to make in the coming years, both professionally and personally.

Frank came into this increasingly toxic atmosphere with his own set of fears and misgivings. Despite the films he had made, the three Academy Awards he had won, the additional Oscar he received for one of his wartime documentaries, and the Distinguished Service Medal he had been given, he was ever aware that he had started life as an immigrant. He was deeply aware of the negative feelings toward immigrants that always seemed to surface in times of strife in America. The treatment of his sister Anne, who had neglected to become a citizen and who was nearly deported during World War II, was never far from his mind.

The displacement of his years away from Hollywood to serve in the army made him feel vulnerable and less sure of himself. He was no longer the brash young man who had stormed Columbia

Pictures and slammed the door in Sam Briskin's face. There were times when he felt more like the little boy selling newspapers in front of the Jonathan Club.

In Hollywood, you were only as good as your last picture. Brief congratulations were given those who had served. Then returning veterans were made to realize that time had moved on, new and younger people had replaced them, and they would have to fight to reinstate themselves.

When Frank Capra returned from his service, he was almost fifty years old. He was starting over, no matter what his previous stature in the industry had been, in a Hollywood that was massively different, in many ways, from the one he had left. The advent of television; the breakup of the studio systems, with its staid allegiances and contracts; and the changing systems of acquisition, production, and distribution would have lasting effects on the industry to which he had contributed so much. It would take energy, determination, grit, and confidence to adjust to the changes.

Although Frank had the desire to begin again, his confidence was shaken. As he himself had often said, "This profession is only for the valiant." He began by creating an independent film company, Liberty Films. His partners were George Stevens, William Wyler, and Sam Briskin. All three had served in the war making documentary films. But there the similarity ended. Capra had spent most of his time in Washington and a little in London, compiling footage into films that were awarded for their expertise and inspiration. Wyler and Stevens had actually been in war zones, experiencing battle and the horrors of war firsthand.

Wyler had flown on many dangerous bombing missions, filming in all parts of the plane and during all aspects of battles. On one mission, he had crawled into the belly of the bomber to get a better shot. He wanted to capture and document the experience from every angle. The noise was unearthly. When the plane landed, he had lost his hearing. He was partially deaf for the rest of his life.

When Wyler returned from the war, he was unsure about how his injury would affect his marriage and his career. He decided to make a film that would directly address, with complete accuracy, the experience of returning veterans. *The Best Years of Our Lives* told the stories of three men: a working-class veteran, a middle-class veteran, and an upper-class veteran. With searing reality and the use of a nonprofessional actor who had lost both hands in a training accident, Wyler laid bare the issues of job loss, familial difficulties, marital strife, and alcoholism in adjusting to life after war, all potentially aspects of what is now called post-traumatic stress disorder (PTSD).

George Stevens, Frank Capra's other partner in Liberty Films, had been a documentary filmmaker in the US Army Signal Corps under Eisenhower. He had been among the first American units to liberate Dachau. The soldiers were utterly unprepared for the level of horror and depravity they witnessed, and the sheer mass scale of death at Dachau. The starvation, disease, and human degradation were staggering. Stevens shot footage for days on end. He felt a crushing responsibility to document what had happened there. There was no aspect he allowed to go undocumented, as an undisputable record of the horror and as proof for future prosecution. Many of the former inmates understood his ultimate purpose and made sure there was no horror he did not document.

Stevens arrived at Dachau in late April and left in early July. He turned to alcohol, then isolation. Friends like Frank Capra and William Wyler tried to interest him in new projects, but he was unable to respond at first. Eventually, Stevens went back to filmmaking. His films ever after reflected, as he said, his trip to the "dark heart of humanity."

Frank had spent the war in Washington, DC, London, and Los Angeles. He experienced a bombing raid in London and saw the devastation and the resilience of the British people. He did not experience battle or the concentration camps firsthand. He returned to his work in Hollywood with a sense that American audiences wanted to be reminded of the common good, the strength of the individual, the support of the community, and the possibility of resurrection through connection with that good.

Frank Capra supported the end of block booking, a practice that had begun in the early days of Hollywood to guarantee the success of films that had less star power by putting them on a bill with higher-profile films. Ironically, the breakup of this system would contribute to the eventual demise of the studio system under which Capra had thrived at Columbia.

To finance Liberty Films, Frank secured a loan from the

Bank of America, founded by another Italian immigrant, A. P. Giannini. He held a press conference on February 23, 1946, to announce that Liberty Films was open for business. Robert Riskin was asked but chose not to be part of the new company. Frank was disappointed but understood Riskin's need for independence. United Artists also passed up the opportunity to be associated with Liberty Films, another example of how Capra's standing in the industry had changed. Finally, RKO came through. Liberty Films agreed to produce under the umbrella of RKO, with each director signed to deliver three films.

Frank searched actively for new properties. He considered and pursued a film about pioneer women and another based on a story by a favorite professor at Cal Tech, Alfred Noyes. Neither came to fruition. Then he was presented with a brief story by Philip Van Doren Stern called "The Greatest Gift." Stern had tried to sell the story in a longer version and had no luck. So he fashioned a shorter version that he printed as Christmas cards to send to family and friends. He sent one to his agent, who sold it to RKO.

Frank optioned it for Liberty in September 1945. By then it had already been developed by such estimable writers as Clifford Odets, Marc Connelly, and Dalton Trumbo. They had all worked on making the story into a screenplay, with varying degrees of success. When Frank optioned it, the project had been put on the shelf by RKO.

The premise was simple: A middle-aged man, depressed and suicidal, has the chance, through an angel, to see what his life, and the lives of those around him, would have been like if he had never lived. By experiencing human connection and good deeds, he is redeemed. The story had a strong appeal to Frank. Charles Dickens' "A Christmas Carol" was one of his favorite pieces of writing; he owned a first edition. On a deeper level, it reflected the state of his own mind at the time.

With the optioning of the property from RKO, Frank Capra began a drive to be recognized not only as a director but as a writer, or at least to be given screen credit. This infuriated some in the industry, who felt that he was demanding more than he deserved. Frank worried that the industry as a whole was beginning to forget him. As an immigrant and a man who had associated with many who were called before HUAC, he was afraid for his future. He was also older in an industry that prized youth. He faced an America that had changed drastically since he had left Hollywood in 1941, at the height of his career.

Frank proceeded with the project that came to be called *It's a Wonderful Life*, believing that America would embrace a film about redemption through the healing power of friendship and community. At its heart, the film also provides a map to the inner torture of the lead actor, Jimmy Stewart, and Frank Capra himself. Stewart was suffering from the consequences of five years spent as a bomber pilot in World War II. His agony as he contemplates suicide is palpable. Frank was grappling from profound questions of displacement, fear, and the insecurity of having to begin a career all over again.

At the conclusion of the film, George Bailey is recognized as a leader and a beloved figure. He is redeemed and healed. Frank Capra sought that recognition and healing, as did Jimmy

Stewart. Both looked to *It's a Wonderful Life* to restart their careers after the devastation of World War II.

Frank hired a number of writers to work on the project. Jo Swerling, Michael Wilson, an ex-Marine who had become a screenwriter, Dorothy Parker, and the married team of Frances Goodrich and Albert Hackett all worked on the script at various times. Wilson, Goodrich, and Hackett in particular did not enjoy their experience. Frank and Swerling ended up rewriting, sometimes at the last moment, and Frank insisted vociferously on having a screen credit, which he eventually got. Some of the speeches Frank wrote, especially those for the depressed George Bailey, had to be cut or deleted. They indicate what must have been his mental state at the time. They are full of intensity and the shame and fear of failure.

Despite his internal misgivings and fears, outwardly Frank approached the film with focus, determination, and a renewed excitement. The set for the town of Bedford Falls was built on the RKO Encino Ranch. It was elaborate and covered almost five acres. New techniques for snow were developed, as so many scenes took place in winter. Engineers developed a way to mix foamite, a material used in fire extinguishers, with soap and water. When pushed out of pipes under high pressure, it looked exactly like fluffy snowfall.

Technicians used 300 tons of gypsum to cover windows and buildings to look like snow and 6,000 gallons of chemicals to create the snow. The day they began shooting the first snowstorm, on June 30, 1946, it was ninety degrees in Encino by noon.

In addition to the crucial Jimmy Stewart, Frank Capra had gathered a cast of some of his favorite actors, many from his stable of great character actors: Henry Travers as Clarence the angel, Thomas Mitchell as Uncle Billy, Frank Faylen as Ernie, Ward Bond as Bert, and Beulah Bondi as Mrs. Bailey. The greatest, however, was Lionel Barrymore, who was now crippled with arthritis. Used to playing lovable characters at this point in his career, he relished playing the grasping, greedy Mr. Potter, even though he had to take hourly shots for his pain. After several actresses Frank approached turned down the role of Mary because they thought it too bland, the beautiful newcomer Donna Reed was chosen.

Frank's relationship with his cast was, as always, joyous and positive. Jimmy Stewart was nervous about shooting the kissing scene in which he declares his undying love for Mary while she is considering a proposal from rival Sam Wainwright. Frank suggested that it be done while Mary is on the phone. They did the scene in one take, and it remains a masterful example of acting, direction and camerawork. The intensity and desperation of George and his deep need for Mary's love are achingly realized; the humanity and authenticity, coupled with the shocked humor of Mary's mother's reaction, are captivating and unforgettable.

Despite the good feelings on the set, the outside world impinged to the degree that HUAC, aided and abetted by the Motion Picture Alliance for the Preservation of American Ideals (MPA), reached its tentacles everywhere. Ward Bond, who played Bert, one of the policemen in Bedford Falls, was virulently anti-Communist. Other cast members were overtly critical of HUAC. Every scene and every script began to be viewed through this lens.

Frank was made aware that there was an innuendo campaign against him and that the HUAC committee had targeted him. This haunted him and added to his sense of insecurity.

Frank had begun *It's a Wonderful Life* working with a new director of photography, Victor Milner, whom he disliked. He eventually begged Harry Cohn and Columbia to allow him to hire Joe Walker. Cohn agreed and Walker returned to work with Capra to finish the film. It was Walker who photographed the final scene of *It's a Wonderful Life*: the gathering of the community of Bedford Falls, the circle of George Bailey's family and friends. The totality of what was important in his life, in one room. The camera moved slowly and lovingly over the group of character actors, many of whom Frank had known for two decades. Fittingly, they sang "Auld Lang Syne."

The scene represented an elegiac pinnacle for Frank Capra and Joe Walker. For nearly twenty years, they had worked together. They had known each other's creative highs and lows, each other's wives and children and family lives. The scene presented a kind of summation of their work together, and they seemed to intrinsically understand that they would never work together again. Frank and Walker had created iconic images of American life as it was and as they hoped it still could be. These images represented their belief that the true American spirit was in the redemptive power of the individual in connection with community.

Frank Capra and Jimmy Stewart celebrated the wrap of the film with an old-fashioned picnic for cast and crew, complete with ice cream sodas and sack races. Due to problems with *Sinbad*, the film that RKO had planned for a holiday release, the studio made the decision to push the opening of *It's a Wonderful Life* to the upcoming holiday. That would give it plenty of time for Oscar contention. Frank was feeling confident; filming was finished and the editing process was well underway. The film looked beautiful and he was sure that Jimmy Stewart's performance would position him well for Best Actor.

Frank was heartened by the experience of *It's a Wonderful Life*. He and William Wyler had entered into a friendly competition at the beginning of filming. Wyler, who was also starting to shoot *The Best Years of Our Lives*, sent Frank a telegram that read "Last one in is a rotten egg." Frank replied, "My first day was easy, but do you know they're using sound these days?"

Frank had entered into shooting *It's a Wonderful Life* with trepidation, but the relief of having finished it was satisfying and reassuring. It had cost nearly $3 million, and now came the job of selling the film to critics and audiences.

The marketing for *It's a Wonderful Life* was decidedly upbeat. It featured holiday themes, a smiling Bailey family, and even a photo of Jimmy Stewart swinging Donna Reed high in the air. The ads made it look like a cross between a family holiday movie and a screwball romance. Nowhere did it mention potential suicide or the darker theme of greed and desperation.

The "private showing" and dinner dance which had become standard for selected major releases postwar was December 9,

1946, at the Ambassador Hotel in Los Angeles. Publicists went all out and fed guests, which included nearly every major star in Hollywood, beef tenderloin and strawberries Romanoff. They danced the night away. Spirits were high.

During the second half of December, major storms set in, keeping people indoors and away from movie theaters. Those who braved the cold waves and winter weather were surprised and disheartened by the somber issues in the film. They went expecting holiday fare. They did not want to see a desperate Jimmy Stewart contemplating suicide.

Some reviews were positive. Others were scathing. The box office, which did not live up to expectations, dropped off sharply after the holidays. It seemed clear that with $3 million spent on the film, the box office receipts were nowhere near what was needed to recoup what had been spent, let alone make much of a profit. This put Liberty films in serious jeopardy.

Frank and Jimmy Stewart, eager to try to pump up the box office, made a publicity trip to Beaumont, Texas, but their plane ran into rough weather and was five hours late for the gala event. By the time they landed, the bands, choral groups and many in the crowd had gone home. One of the first questions Frank was asked was about how Hollywood felt about Communists. Frank responded by praising the patriotism of Hollywood and declaring his own. But the question was an unsettling reminder of what was on small town America's mind.

Frank and Jimmy Stewart still allowed themselves to hope for Oscar wins. Both were previous winners, Stewart for *Philadelphia Story* and Frank for *It Happened One Night, Mr.*

Deeds Goes to Town, You Can't Take It With You, and the wartime documentary *Prelude to War*. But this was a new era and a new generation. Both men felt they wanted to prove themselves as winners in the postwar era. It would let the world know that they were relevant, that they had come through. That they had exorcised their demons and made something their peers in the industry recognized as superior and meaningful.

"We have done this so many times, Lu," said Frank as they prepared to go to the Academy Awards on March 13, 1947. "Are the kids aware?"

"Aware?" said Lu. "Frank Jr. has been talking of nothing else for a week. He is thirteen years old and . . . and, well thirteen-year-old boys are sensitive to their fathers. Or at least your thirteen-year-old boy is."

"I guess I hadn't noticed," admitted Frank, "I confess I've been preoccupied. It's terrible, you know. Once you get into this vortex, you just can't get out until it is all, finally, over."

"I know, Frank. We all know," said Lu.

They swept down the stairs of the house in Brentwood. Lulu, now ten, stood in the foyer, looking up at her father. Frank was struck by how much she resembled her mother.

"I have something for you," Lulu said, "like Zuzu in the movie."

She handed Frank three petals from a purple narcissus in their garden. It had just bloomed and the fragrance was intoxicating. Frank put them in his pocket and bent down to kiss his daughter.

"You are not a movie daughter," he said. "You are the real thing. So much better."

"Good luck, Daddy," she said solemnly.

A limousine was waiting to take Lu and Frank to the ceremony, which was being held at the Shrine Auditorium in downtown L.A. Frank could see Lulu's face as they pulled out of the driveway. She waved and stared after them until they disappeared into the misty Los Angeles evening.

As they made their way downtown, Frank thought of Manual Arts High School, located not far away from the Shrine. As they alighted from the shiny black car, he was reminded of seeing the Pasadena girls get out of their parents' cars. He could feel himself staring out the window of the high school in his janitor's clothing, wanting to belong, to be part of their world.

Lu and Frank were surrounded immediately by well-wishers and old friends. *It's a Wonderful Life* had been nominated for five Academy Awards. Frank was smiling, full of outward confidence and love for the industry. But inside, he was full of the doubt that had propelled George Bailey.

Frank could see the way the evening was going to go when Harold Russell, the actor who had played the disabled veteran in *The Best Years of Our Lives*, won the Oscar for Best Supporting Actor. William Wyler's film swept the awards, with additional wins for Wyler as Best Director, Fredric March for Best Actor, and Best Picture, Film Editing, and Screenplay.

Frank was happy for his friend and partner William Wyler. But because *The Best Years of Our Lives* was produced by Samuel

Goldwyn, there would be no financial reward for Liberty Films. Frank had been wrong about the American public and what they wanted to see. They wanted to address the realities of a war that had changed their lives forever.

Lu and Frank attended a party afterward. They were gracious and congratulatory. As they were leaving, Joan Crawford leaned down to whisper in Frank's ear, "I've won. And I've lost. It's always more fun to win. Don't forget your film is extraordinary. I loved every frame of it. Get back on the horse, Frank Capra."

They drove home in silence. Lu held Frank's hand.

"I'm selling Liberty Films. I've decided," said Frank.

"I'm with you no matter what you do, Frank," said Lu.

He pulled the flower petals Lulu had given him out of his pocket. Frank and Lu looked at them as the limousine pulled into their driveway.

"The children are with you, too," Lu said. "You made the movie you wanted to make. That is what matters. That is what you will remember."

On April 7, 1948, Frank Capra sat behind President Harry Truman as the president watched an exclusive screening of Frank's next film, *State of the Union*. Lu sat on one side and Bess Truman on the other.

Frank was thankful to be able to come and go during the screening, as his nerves dictated that he couldn't sit in one place. The event had been arranged by MGM, the studio that had loaned Paramount two of its stars for the film, Spencer Tracy and Katherine Hepburn. Frank had sold Liberty Films to Paramount, and they had exacted a three-picture deal from him.

He was now beholden to Paramount Pictures. Frank recalled the angry reception *Mr. Smith Goes to Washington* had received and was fearful of repeating the incident. Adding to his anxiety was the fact that the times were different. Although *State of the Union* poked fun at all forms of demagoguery, the HUAC investigations had made everything more volatile.

Written by Howard Lindsay and Russell Crouse, *State of the Union* had been a hit on Broadway. The story of an ambivalent businessman who is talked into running for president and ultimately injected with integrity by his wife, the film was planned to star Spencer Tracy and Claudette Colbert. Days before shooting was to begin, Colbert made a demand about having to stop work each day at precisely 5:00 p.m., saying that she felt and looked too tired after that time to be effective. The demand was untenable due to budget and schedule considerations. Colbert was out.

Spencer Tracy suggested as a last-minute replacement the woman with whom he had had a professional and personal partnership for years, Katharine Hepburn. She agreed to do the film and came to the rescue. She was a great, singular star, and Frank relished the opportunity to work with her. However, she came to the film with her own baggage, affected by HUAC and the political tenor of the time.

This had nothing to do with demands or contracts. It was well known in Hollywood that Hepburn was descended from a long line of progressive thinkers. She came from a wealthy family and had attended Bryn Mawr College. Her mother was a campaigner for social justice and had taken Katherine to Votes for Women demonstrations as a young girl. Her father was a noted urologist, and all of the Hepburn children were encouraged to speak their minds.

A few months prior to the start of *State of the Union*, Hepburn had made a well publicized speech at Gilmore Stadium in Los Angeles on behalf of Henry A. Wallace, a Democrat who was considering a run for president. Only two weeks before that, J. Parnell Thomas, a Republican congressman from New Jersey and chair of HUAC, had come to Hollywood to announce the investigations of Communist infiltration there. Hepburn was furious and decried HUAC, proclaiming the right and necessity of the artist to be free to speak out against injustice.

Liberals applauded her stance, but studio heads like Louis B. Mayer were aghast. They feared a backlash at the box office. Hedda Hopper, the powerful gossip columnist, unleashed endless criticism. Stones were hurled at the screen when Hepburn's latest film, *Sea of Grass*, premiered in North Carolina.

Also in the cast of *State of the Union* was Adolph Menjou, an actor who had been a favorite of Frank's. He had appeared in two previous films with Hepburn. Menjou was a virulent anti-Communist and a staunch Republican who actively claimed that Hollywood was one of the centers of Communist activity in America. A leading member of the Motion Picture Alliance for the Preservation of American Ideals, a group formed to oppose Communist influence in Hollywood, he had been more than happy to provide to HUAC lists of actors, directors, and writers he suspected of being Communists.

On the *State of the Union* set, the tension between Hepburn, who despised everything Menjou stood for, and Menjou, who said about Hepburn, "Scratch a do-gooder like Hepburn and they'll yell Pravda," was palpable. Frank did what he could to diffuse it. Knowing that journalists and publicists were lying in wait for a good story, he banned them from the set.

Hepburn was confident in her stance and her background; as she said, her family "practically came over on the *Mayflower*." Frank was less confident and deeply disturbed by the probings of HUAC. His family had come over in steerage on the SS *Germania*. He was an immigrant who had never had the luxury of entitlement. Awareness of the tension and the potential for negative publicity only increased Frank's paranoia. Creating a film that skewered politicians while making serious points about integrity was brave if not foolhardy. A sense of exhaustion, something he hadn't previously experienced on film sets, sometimes overcame him. One night, early in the shoot, he invited Spencer Tracy to look at rushes and had nothing to say to the actor. Tracy took it as an insult and was furious. Stomach troubles, always a sign of tension and anxiety, began to plague Frank.

He was immensely relieved when, at the conclusion of the *State of the Union* screening, President Truman turned to him and congratulated him. He seemed genuinely pleased and charmed by the film. Frank's fears of outright rejection were unfounded, and *State of the Union* did relatively well at the box office. But the feeling of fear lingered. The courage, confidence, and certainty that had propelled him throughout his career were shaken.

The next three years at Paramount proved to Frank that being under the yoke of a major studio was not conducive to his best work. The time was filled with projects proposed and projects jettisoned, often due to budget. He directed two films starring Bing Crosby, *Riding High*, a remake of *Broadway Bill*, and *Here Comes the Groom*. The actors he worked with continued to find him full of life, willing to listen to ideas, and completely respectful of them.

Alexis Smith, a young actress who admired Frank greatly and who costarred in *Here Comes the Groom*, was shocked to hear him say one day that he was considering giving up directing. He explained that the problem wasn't being on the set, working with actors and creating together. That was the part he loved. For these two films, for example, he had thrown out the usual way of producing a musical number, which was to record a stiff and disconnected "perfect" recording on a soundstage and then have the actors lip-synch to it in playback on set. Frank had the actors sing in the moment and recorded and filmed them live. The result was a much more natural and absorbing performance. The part that Frank Capra abhorred was dealing with the money men.

Here Comes the Groom was based on a story by Robert Riskin and Liam O'Brien. Capra and Riskin had once been the closest of friends. By this point, their relationship was respectful but wary. Shooting on the film was underway when Riskin suffered a major stroke on December 27, 1950. He was never fully himself again.

Lu and Frank Capra began to discuss the idea of moving

permanently away from Brentwood. They talked about the possibility of living on Silver Lake in the High Sierra, where they had recently built a large home. They discussed moving to Fallbrook and Red Mountain Ranch, where they owned property that included a large reservoir and a home built by Stanford White.

In late 1948, Frank Capra made a rash decision to sell his entire rare books collection. It had been a symbol of his move away from the illiterate family that had raised him. He had come so far, and yet the things that once gave him pleasure and an assured place in the world seemed to mock him. He sold it without warning for a quarter of what it was worth and when Lu, shocked, asked why, he said, "I hate them all."

Chapter Eleven

THE EMBRACE OF REDEMPTION

"I'm fourteen years old and I didn't want to leave my friends, my school, and everything I know to move to this stupid little town!" Lulu wailed. "I hate it. I hate all of it!"

She slammed out of the car and walked slowly toward the dusty yard that surrounded her new school in Fallbrook, a community in Riverside County about 130 miles from Los Angeles. For Lulu, it might as well have been a thousand miles away. It was a far cry from the exclusive Westlake School for Girls in Bel Air.

Frank pulled out of the driveway to the school and headed toward the highway. He was going to a meeting at Caltech, formerly Throop College of Technology, his alma mater. He supposed they wanted him to donate money. He decided to stop by the ranch to see if the mail had come. He was waiting for a security clearance letter that would allow him to work for Project Vista.

In April of 1951, Frank and Lu Capra had sold their Brentwood estate and moved their family to Red Mountain Ranch near Fallbrook, California. Their hope was to give themselves, their marriage, and their family a respite from the pressures of Hollywood. They wanted to make a new start. Frank had been released from his contract with Paramount after making his final film for them, *Here Comes the Groom*. He would not make another film for seven years.

Frank had served his country willingly during World War II, and the return to creative life after the war had proved to be full of conflict and insecurity. The HUAC investigations, which caused havoc and ruined many relationships, rattled his confidence. He seemed to lose touch with what audiences wanted to see.

The Capras' new life in Fallbrook was full of joyful moments and difficult adjustments. As he did with every challenge, Frank plunged into life at Red Mountain Ranch with all the energy he could muster. He hoped to pour all his creative force into working with the land, much as his father had done.

Initially, the Capra family joined in where they could. Fallbrook was a small farming community. Lulu and Tom went to public schools. Frank joined the school board and got to know the people in town, spending long hours speaking with everyone from farmers to businesspeople to city officials. Lu worked at the Angels Thrift Store as a volunteer. The family had film nights in their basement recreation room, where they showed Capra films to family and friends.

The transition from a high-profile, luxurious, and sophisticated life in Hollywood, with all the trappings of celebrity culture and attention, was not always easy. Some Fallbrook locals remained skeptical and saw the Capras as outsiders. Lu suffered physically from allergies to the local flora. Frank threw himself into farming. He planted trees and orchards and developed methodical ways to chart the growth of each plant. He hoped that living at the ranch and farming the land would replace the sense of emptiness that sometimes overcame him.

Frank had been pleased to be contacted by Project Vista, a top-secret government study, about being part of their work. Named for the Vista del Arroyo Hotel in Pasadena, where meetings were held, Project Vista was formed to study warfare in all its permutations, including ground, air, and nuclear, with special respect to the defense of Western Europe. There was interest in including thinkers from a wide variety of backgrounds, and both military and civilian participants were considered. Everyone involved had to have a security clearance, due to the sensitivity of the topics that would be studied. The security clearance was expected to be quick and easy. Nevertheless, Frank was anxious about it and hoped every day for a letter that would give him the official word.

On the morning of December 9, 1951, he stopped at home before leaving for Pasadena. A thick, official-looking envelope had arrived. Lu sat, smoking one of her cigarettes and watching Frank as he opened the packet. It didn't take him long to find the answer he was looking for.

His security clearance had been denied. The packet contained copies of files going back to 1932, when the FBI had begun to investigate him. Frank silently looked through the files. And then it began. A flood of tears. Tears of anger and shame.

Lu hadn't seen her husband cry since the night they met and he told her about his father's death. He hadn't allowed himself to cry when Johnny died. He had been strong for her. Held her up. Now she had to be strong for him. It was all nonsense, of course. No one was more patriotic than her husband. No one loved his country more than Frank. No one had championed the value of democracy and the freedom of the individual more than her husband.

"We are going to fight this, darling. Do you hear me?" she said after a time. "You are going to call our lawyer and John Ford and anyone we can think of who will write a letter for you. We are not going to let this stand."

Frank holed up with Chet Sticht, the man who had been his assistant for nearly thirty years, in an office he had built on the grounds of Red Mountain Ranch. They worked for weeks, even over Christmas that year, to craft a 220 page rebuttal. It was an outraged response that detailed everything Frank believed about America and his contributions to the artistic and political life of his adopted country, not to mention his war effort. The fact that not six years before he had been given the highest honor a civilian can receive from the military made the situation all the more outrageous, devastating, and humiliating.

One day, on a winding road near Red Mountain Ranch, like characters in *Miracle Woman*, *Lost Horizon*, *Meet John Doe*, and *It's a Wonderful Life*, Frank Capra contemplated suicide. He realized he could just drive off the edge of the steep mountain road.

He looked down at the seat next to him. Lulu had left one of her schoolbooks. Tucked inside was a paper she had written.

Frank slid it out and read, "This is what America means to me. The freedom to be anything, to do anything. To come on a ship from Italy, like my dad, and then to tell stories with movies."

Frank looked out at the horizon. The sun was beginning to set and shadows fell across the foothills leading to Red Mountain. He had not lost the will to live. He saw the faces of Lu, Frank Jr., Lulu, and Tom. He kept the car on the road and returned home.

He received a partial security clearance on January 7, nearly a month later. In the intervening time, he had gathered letters from prominent directors, actors, and military personnel who had worked with him, including General George C. Marshall. The experience had changed him forever. It had profoundly shaken his faith in one of the things he valued most: his citizenship in the country he loved.

Soon after, Frank was contacted by AT&T about making a series of science films that would be factual, educational, and entertaining. From 1952 to 1958, he commuted to an office in Beverly Hills and made four films that combined his love of science and art. The films were *Our Mr. Sun*, *Hemo the Magnificent*, *The Strange Case of the Cosmic Rays*, and *The Unchained Goddess*. Even AT&T was not immune from the effects of the McCarthy era. They insisted that Capra sign a contract clause saying no blacklisted writers would be hired to work on the project. When asked why he didn't make features anymore, Frank Capra replied, "Communism isn't funny."

Frank and Lu became increasingly religious during this time, returning to the deep roots of Catholicism and spirituality that would have delighted Frank's mother, Sarrida. He and Lu

Capra were remarried in a ceremony at the Catholic church in Fallbrook. Their children looked on with amusement and love.

In September 1955, Robert Riskin died after living for five years in increasingly diminished physical and mental capacity. Frank did not attend his funeral. He had called when Riskin was taken ill initially but had not visited him. He said he felt unwelcome.

The complicated relationship between the two titans of their world, both acknowledged as having achieved at the highest levels of their profession, reflected the differences in their political views and in their emotional lives. When it was strongest, the synergy between them resulted in some of the most cherished moments in cinema. But the bitterness and disappointment born of internal differences and external pressures caused schisms that couldn't be bridged.

Riskin, known for his kindness, gentility, wit, and concern for others, bristled one day near the end of his life when a visitor, writer Sidney Buchman, criticized Frank Capra for not coming to visit him. Riskin, ever loyal, turned his wheelchair to Buchman and said, "He is my best friend."

A final struggle loomed involving Red Mountain Ranch. A large reservoir on the property became the focus of a water rights dispute worthy of a story premise for a Frank Capra film. Ultimately, Camp Pendleton and other government agencies became involved, as the dispersal of water affected government land and property. It became, in Frank's mind, a fight between the "little guy" and big government. He became a member of the water rights board and considered running for office. But not everyone in the community saw Frank Capra as a "little guy." To them, he still had the patina of wealth and privilege.

Frank had found that even at idyllic Red Mountain Ranch, strife and challenge followed him. He couldn't let go of the insecurity born of the years of watching his back, of considering and reconsidering every creative decision, whether he wanted to or not, under the prism of whether it would offend HUAC. This insecurity haunted and eventually handicapped him.

Max Youngstein, a former vice president at Paramount and now vice president at United Artists, had a soft spot for Frank Capra. He encouraged him to come back to Hollywood.

The Hollywood to which Frank returned had undergone a massive change in power structure. It was a new world. The property was the film *A Hole in the Head*, based on Arnold Shulman's Broadway play. Put together by agent Abe Lastfogel, the project was produced in the "new" way, with Frank Sinatra, the star, getting two-thirds of the profit and Frank Capra one-third. In addition, Sinatra was a coproducer, which meant he had input on the script, casting, and final cut.

Although Frank Capra had lost none of his ability to work with actors, he was so determined to bring the production in under budget that his work was rushed and sometimes unfocused. It was difficult and galling to accept the power that Sinatra wielded. Sinatra famously did only one take of each scene; Edward G. Robinson worked in exactly the opposite way, wanting to do take after take. "High Hopes," the song written for the film by Sammy Cahn, became a kind of anthem for Frank Capra.

In 1960, Frank was asked to be part of the Sixth Annual National Strategy Seminar at the US Army War College in Pennsylvania. His security clearance was revisited. Nearly ten years of humiliation ended on February 24, 1960, when he was granted a full security clearance.

The exhaustion of having to prove his loyalty over and over during those years had taken its toll. Throughout, Frank kept proposing projects to various studios. He once traveled to Italy to begin work on a film with John Wayne. But he left the project when he realized Wayne's outsized ego and his own lack of power to confront it. The courage and confidence needed to helm groundbreaking works of art eluded him.

The 1960s saw Frank Capra take on the mantle of ambassador and speaker. He attended conferences, symposiums, and United States Information Agency (USIA) events, always speaking about the power and beauty of American democracy and the fundamental importance of the artist being able to create away from the strictures of tyranny. Most of all, he championed the extraordinary power of the American cinema to extend the message of hope and freedom throughout the world.

He was invited to a luncheon with President John F. Kennedy, receiving the invitation on the day of Kennedy's assassination. He met President Lyndon Johnson and went golfing with President Gerald Ford on Ford's 78th birthday in 1975. Frank couldn't help contemplating what his parents would have thought.

In all of his meetings and presentations during these years,

Frank often stressed that the artist cannot be political. And yet he made one of the most political films of all time, *Mr. Smith Goes to Washington*. When the people of France were asked which film they wanted to see at the end of World War II, they voted over-whelmingly for *Mr. Smith Goes to Washington*. In the years since it was first seen, politicians of all stripes and beliefs have quoted from the film and held it up as one that defines democracy and what it means to be an American. This curious contradiction summed up the inherent struggle that seemed to define Frank's life after the war.

Frank Capra made his final studio feature in 1961. *Pocketful of Miracles* was a remake of *Lady for a Day*, a film he first made in 1933. This time, the glowing simplicity, heart-wrenching climax, and witty repartee of the former film were nowhere to be found. They had been replaced by actors who had been "packaged" and were doing the film only for the money.

Frank experienced cluster headaches. Helped by his son Frank Jr., who had become a director in his own right, he managed to finish the shoot. Out of sheer grit, and with shots of sodium pentothal administered secretly, he finished the film on time and within budget.

Frank's inner turmoil was belied by the honors bestowed on him by an industry that had not forgotten him. May 12, 1962, was proclaimed Frank Capra Day in Los Angeles by Mayor Sam Yorty. Frank was feted with a dinner and laudatory speeches by his friends John Ford and Jimmy Stewart. This accolade was added to the George Eastman Award for Distinguished Contribution to the Art of Film he received in 1957, his Distinguished Alumni Award from Caltech in 1966, and the Golden Anchor Award from the US Naval Reserve's Combat Camera Group in 1975 for his World War II photography and filmmaking.

In March of 1971, Frank and Lu Capra were traveling through the Panama Canal when they received word that Frank's autobiography, *The Name Above the Title*, had been chosen as a Book-of-the-Month Club selection. Frank got roaring drunk in celebration and when he woke up the next day, his cluster headaches were gone, never to return. He had been recognized, finally, as the sole author of a book. The success of the book and the attention it received revived him. He went on book tours and spoke to college and university students.

That same year, the Capras sold Red Mountain Ranch, giving part of it to Caltech as a retreat for research and conferences. They moved to La Quinta, California, to enjoy the ease and beauty they found there. There, in rooms overlooking the Santa Rosa Mountains, they were visited by family and friends without the worry of having to care for a large property.

With the publication of his autobiography, Frank became an ambassador for film. His many awards, including his three Academy Awards for Best Director and the Oscar he had received for *Prelude to War*, recognized his excellence in his industry. He had been president of the Academy and the Screen Directors Guild, voted to these positions by peers. He received an honorary doctorate from Wesleyan University in 1981, the American Film Institute (AFI) Life Achievement Award in 1982, and the National Medal of Arts in 1986.

In 1977, Frank traveled for the first time back to Bisacquino, Italy. He was 80 years old and in poor health. The crowds and heat made him want only one thing: to go home.

His home was now America. He was an American. He had become an American not only by getting his citizenship, but by forging a life of creating films that expressed his love for his country and his empathy for the American people. His parents had left the little town in Sicily seventy-four years earlier for new lives inspired by the promise of freedom. His father, Turridu, had pointed out the torch held high by Lady Liberty when they came into New York Harbor, saying "See, Cici? It is the light of freedom."

Frank Capra had fulfilled the promise. In a life replete with success and recognition, he had also battled profound tragedy and disappointment. He had faced challenges brought on by war, politics of the time, and the vicissitudes of life in all its mystery. Through it all, he maintained that humanism and human connection made life worth living. We can only experience the profound joy on George Bailey's face because we have also experienced the depth of his despair and sorrow. The hope in his eyes becomes our hope.

On July 1, 1984, Frank sat by Lu's bedside. He held her hand as her breathing grew more labored. The bougainvillea she had always loved, since the night they met at the Hotel Del, hung in bowers outside the open window. The room was suffused with the soft light of the early morning. The children and grandchildren, who had faithfully come day after day, hadn't yet arrived. Their pictures hung on the walls: births, marriages, graduations, baptisms, each one a part of life's beautiful cycle. Frank leaned down and kissed Lu as she slipped away. There was no doubt in his mind; this kind of love, this human connection, was worth striving for, worth hoping for, worth embracing.

Frank Capra passed away peacefully in his home, surrounded by his children and grandchildren, on September 3, 1991. He was ninety-four years old. He had embraced the ideal that each human can find a place of wholeness and humanity. His films encourage us to keep striving for that ideal, and his life inspires us to never rest until we achieve it. His example, both as a creative artist and a human being, invites us to believe in the power of the individual and the capability of each and every one of us to affect our families, our communities, and our world for the common good.

Perhaps the frequent contradiction between how he felt on the inside and what happened on the outside spoke to a lifelong truth about Frank Capra. The artistic gift he gave was born in the struggle and poverty of a peasant boy on the streets of Los Angeles. The parades and dinners and speeches honoring him more often than not took place only minutes from the place where had had, as a young and vulnerable immigrant, walked the streets in the early dawn selling newspapers.

He brought all of his life experience into his work as an artist; in the redemptive glance of Anne of Austria in *Fultah Fisher's Boarding House*, the vast loneliness of Morris Goldfish in *The Younger Generation*, the whimsicality of Stew Smith in *Platinum Blonde*, the desire of Kay Arnold in *Ladies of Leisure*, the joy on Peter Warne's face as he sings "The Daring Young Man on the Flying Trapeze" in *It Happened One Night*, the anguish of George Bailey as he contemplates suicide in *It's a Wonderful Life*.

Frank Capra lived with the contradictions of human existence and explored them with depth, humor, authenticity, and love. His empathy allows us all to feel more whole, more human. A vast number of the characters in his films find themselves in situations they didn't expect. They use all of their humanity to triumph. The little boy who came to America from Italy on the SS *Germania* gave us the greatest gift of all: a celebration of the joy in life and, for the darker times, hope for a brighter future.

About the Author

Kate Fuglei is an actress, singer, and writer. She created a one-woman show, *Rachel Calof*, based on the memoir of a Jewish homesteader, and has performed it around America. It won Best Musical at the 2015 United Solo Festival in New York City. Kate has appeared in more than forty roles in episodic television and film, and she was in the First National Broadway tour of *Spring Awakening*. Based in Los Angeles, she has played leading roles in regional theaters across the country, among them Arena Stage, the Public Theater in New York City, and the La Jolla Playhouse. Two of Kate's short stories appeared in *Sister-WriterEaters*, a book of essays about motherhood and food. Kate is the author of *Fermi's Gifts: A Novel Based on the Life of Enrico Fermi* and *The Soul of a Child: A Novel Based on the Life of Maria Montessori*. For more information about Kate, please visit katefuglei.com.

Building Wealth 101
How to Make Your Money Work for You
by Robert Barbera

Character is What Counts
A Novel Based on the Life of Vince Lombardi
by Jonathan Brown

Christopher Columbus: His Life and Discoveries
by Mario Di Giovanni

Dark Labyrinth
A Novel Based on the Life of Galileo Galilei
by Peter David Myers

Defying Danger
A Novel Based on the Life of Father Matteo Ricci
by Nicole Gregory

The Divine Proportions of Luca Pacioli
A Novel Based on the Life of Luca Pacioli
by W.A.W. Parker

Dreams of Discovery
A Novel Based on the Life of the Explorer John Cabot
by Jule Selbo

The Faithful
A Novel Based on the Life of Giuseppe Verdi
by Collin Mitchell

Fermi's Gifts
A Novel Based on the Life of Enrico Fermi
by Kate Fuglei

First Among Equals
A Novel Based on the Life of Cosimo de' Medici
by Francesco Massaccesi

God's Messenger
A Novel Based on the Life of Mother Frances X. Cabrini
by Nicole Gregory

Grace Notes
A Novel Based on the Life of Henry Mancini
by Stacia Raymond

Harvesting the American Dream
A Novel Based on the Life of Ernest Gallo
by Karen Richardson

Humble Servant of Truth
A Novel Based on the Life of Thomas Aquinas
by Margaret O'Reilly

Relentless Visionary: Alessandro Volta
by Michael Berick

Ride Into the Sun
A Novel Based on the Life of Scipio Africanus
by Patric Verrone

Rita Levi-Montalcini
Pioneer & Ambassador of Science
by Francesca Valente

Saving the Republic
A Novel Based on the Life of Marcus Cicero
by Eric D. Martin

Sinner, Servant, Saint
A Novel Based on the Life of St. Francis of Assisi
by Margaret O'Reilly

Soldier, Diplomat, Archaeologist
A Novel Based on the Bold Life of Louis Palma di Cesnola
by Peg A. Lamphier, PhD

The Soul of a Child
A Novel Based on the Life of Maria Montessori
by Kate Fuglei

What a Woman Can Do
A Novel Based on the Life of Artemisia Gentileschi
by Peg A. Lamphier, PhD

FUTURE TITLES FROM THE MENTORIS PROJECT

Novels Based on the Lives of:
Amerigo Vespucci
Antonin Scalia
Antonio Meucci
Buzzie Bavasi
Cesare Beccaria
Father Eusebio Francisco Kino
Federico Fellini
Guido d'Arezzo
Harry Warren
Leonardo Fibonacci
Maria Gaetana Agnesi
Peter Rodino
Pietro Belluschi
Saint Augustine of Hippo

For more information on these titles and
the Mentoris Project, please visit
www.mentorisproject.org

CPSIA information can be obtained
at www.ICGtesting.com
Printed in the USA
LVHW050940030422
715183LV00003B/302